# Right into Reading

A Phonics-Based Reading and Comprehension Program

Jane Ervin

**Book 1**

 **Educators Publishing Service**
Cambridge and Toronto

## About the Author

Jane Ervin works in Washington, D.C., with children with reading and learning differences, and advises parents on educational concerns. Dr. Ervin has written more than 20 books for students, teachers, and parents; her workbooks have sold over 5 million copies. She received her Ed.D. and postdoctoral diploma from UCLA.

## Acknowledgements

I would like to thank the numerous teachers and students with whom I have worked for their encouragement and suggestions during the development of this program. Special thanks to Jo Ann Dyer, who has been involved in so many of my projects, for her errorless manuscripts as well as her enthusiastic support. Thanks also to the production team: Wendy Drexler for her editorial work and painstaking attention to detail; Tatjana Mai-Wyss for her appealing illustrations; and Joyce Weston for her assistance in the cover design and layout of the workbook.

# CONTENTS

# Part One

# Short Vowels, Blends, and Syllables

## Lesson 1: The Letters in the Alphabet

There are 2 kinds of letters in the alphabet.

The **vowels** are **a e i o u** and sometimes **y** and **w**.
The **consonants** are all the other letters.

Circle the vowels.

a    b    c    d    e    f    g    h    i

j    k    l    m    n    o    p    q

r    s    t    u    v    w    x    y    z

Circle the vowels in each word.

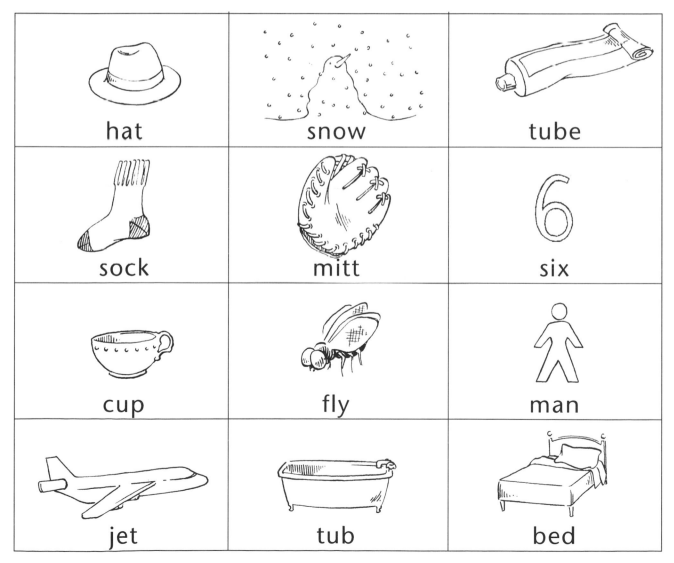

| | | |
|---|---|---|
| hat | snow | tube |
| sock | mitt | six |
| cup | fly | man |
| jet | tub | bed |

➔ Circle the letter that does not belong in each line.

| a | u | e | s | o |
|---|---|---|---|---|
| t | p | i | b | g |
| h | a | x | r | m |
| u | d | o | i | e |

➔ Write the letters in the consonant or vowel box.

g   r   o   j   e   a   t   u   q   l

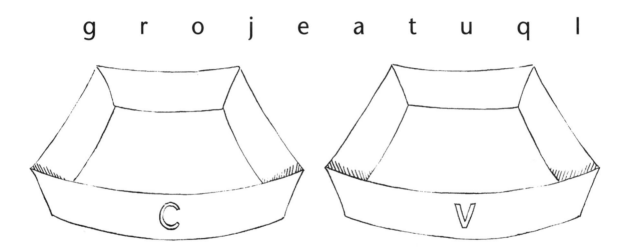

➔ Circle the words that begin with a vowel.

| cat | ant | cup |
|-----|-----|-----|
| egg | hill | pet |
| mad | sad | add |
| Pat | Jon | Eve |

➔ Draw a line between the same vowels.

| | | | | | |
|---|---|---|---|---|---|
| a | o | i | e | o | i |
| e | a | e | i | u | o |
| o | e | u | u | i | u |

➔ Circle the vowel in each word.

Sam has a bat.

Jill can run fast.

Ed had a pet cat.

✎ Write the vowels.

_____, _____, _____, _____,
_____,

and sometimes _____ and _____.

## Lesson 2:  Short Vowel a

Vowels are **short** when there is **one vowel** followed by **only consonants**.

hat

Sound out the letters to read each word.

| | | | |
|---|---|---|---|
| at | an | am | and |
| cat | can | dad | sad |
| man | hat | nap | ran |
| had | pal | mad | ham |

| | | | |
|---|---|---|---|
| fat | tag | Pam | rack |
| wax | rap | back | last |
| cab | pat | tan | fast |
| sack | wag | tax | yam |

Learn to read these words:  **as  has     is  his     was  the**

➔ Draw a line between the words that rhyme.

| | | | | | |
|---|---|---|---|---|---|
| tan | bat | wag | tag | man | has |
| rat | can | wax | tax | as | fan |
| sad | mad | van | ham | nap | lab |
| pat | bat | jam | man | cab | rap |

→ Circle the name of the picture.

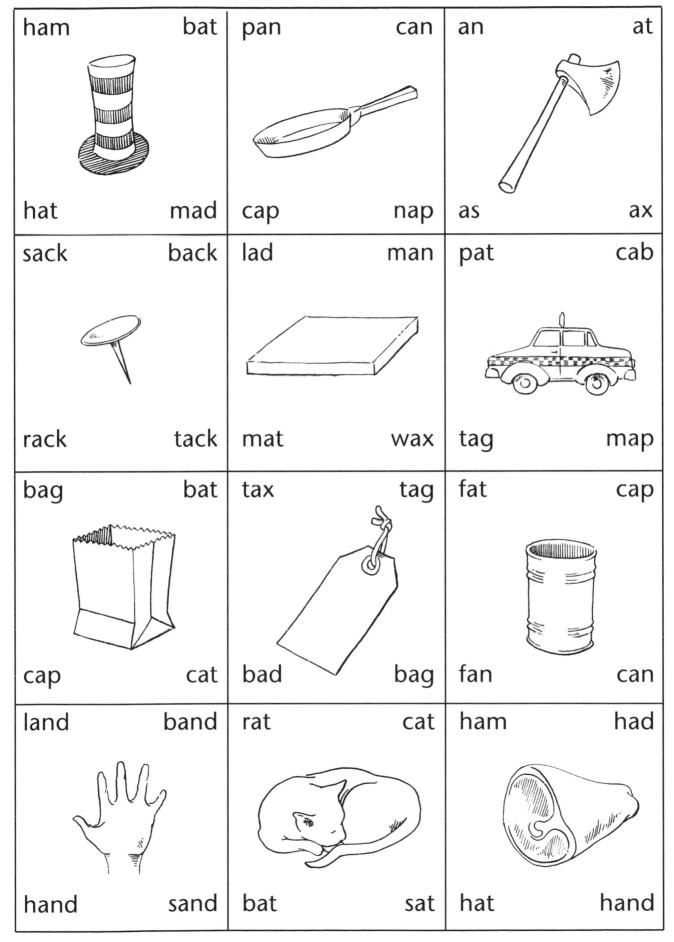

| ham          bat | pan          can | an          at |
| hat          mad | cap          nap | as          ax |
| sack        back | lad          man | pat        cab |
| rack        tack | mat          wax | tag        map |
| bag          bat | tax          tag | fat        cap |
| cap          cat | bad          bag | fan        can |
| land        band | rat          cat | ham        had |
| hand        sand | bat          sat | hat        hand |

➜ Add a short **a** to find the name of each picture. Write the
number of the picture in the box.

☐ p__n ☐ r__t ☐ w__x ☐ d__d

☐ p__ck ☐ j__m ☐ f__st ☐ n__p

1

2

3

4

5

6

7

8

➜ Change the letters. Then read the new word.

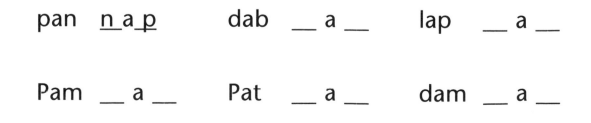

pan  <u>n</u> a <u>p</u>     dab  __ a __     lap  __ a __

Pam  __ a __     Pat  __ a __     dam  __ a __

➜ Read the sentence and circle the missing word. Then write the word on the line.

1. Pass Pat the yams and _____.     hat     had     ham

2. Ann had a _____ at camp.     lap     pal     pat

3. The bag had a _____.     sag     tag     tan

4. Can Jack _____?     at     and     add

5. Dan has a bad _____.     bat     back     lack

6. Mac is Pam's _____.     dad     bad     sad

7. A man has a _____.     sand     land     hand

8. Pack the _____.     tags     bags     rags

→ Put an X in the box next to the sentence that tells about the picture.

☐ Max ran past Nat. Max is fast.

☐ Mac has a hat. Mac ran last.

☐ Pam had a nap.

☐ Nan had a map.

☐ Sam was mad. The rat had his bat.

☐ Jack was sad. The cat had his rat.

☐ Al packs his bag.

☐ Dan tags his bags.

# Pam, Sam, and Tam

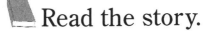 Read the story.

Pam is a cat. Pam has a hat.

Sam is a rat. Sam has a cap.

Tam is a bat. And Tam is fat.

→ Circle the correct answer.

1. Sam is   (a) a cat  (b) a rat  (c) a bat

2. Tam is   (a) a cat  (b) a rat  (c) fat

3. Pam has   (a) a bat  (b) a hat  (c) a rat

✎ Write a story with the words. Then read the story. Check to see that it makes sense. The first story is done for you.

cat    nap    The    a    had

*The cat had a nap.*

ran    rat    The    fast

_____

bat    a    The    has    cap

_____

# A Fast Cab

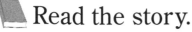 Read the story.

Sam's dad has a cab. Nan's dad has a van.
The cab is fast and can pass the van.

→ Circle the correct answer.

1. Sam's dad has a   (a) cat  (b) cab  (c) van

2. Nan's dad has a   (a) cab  (b) van  (c) tan

3. The cab is   (a) last  (b) past  (c) fast

✎ Write a story with the words. Then read the story to see that it makes sense.

dad    Sam's    man    The    is

_____

- - - - - - - - - - - - - - - - - - - - - - - - - - - - - - - - - - - -

_____ •

Max    Ann    fast    and    ran

_____

- - - - - - - - - - - - - - - - - - - - - - - - - - - - - - - - - - - -

_____ •

ant    has    An    fan    a

_____

- - - - - - - - - - - - - - - - - - - - - - - - - - - - - - - - - - - -

_____ •

# Dan and Tab

 Read the story.

     Dan has a pal. His pal is Tab. Tab is a fat, tan cat. Tab has a rat. Dan pats Tab.

→ Circle the correct answer.

1. Dan's pal is  (a) an ant  (b) a rat  (c) a cat

2. Dan's pal is  (a) Pam  (b) Tam  (c) Tab

3. Tab has  (a) a mat  (b) a hat  (c) a rat

4. Tab has  (a) a pat  (b) a tap  (c) a tag

✎ Write a story with the words. Then read the story to see that it makes sense.

**Tab    Dan's    is    pal**

_____

----------------------------------------------------

_____ •

**Yan    past    ran    Pam**

_____

----------------------------------------------------

_____ •

**the    pack    Can    Jack    bags**

_____

----------------------------------------------------

_____ ?

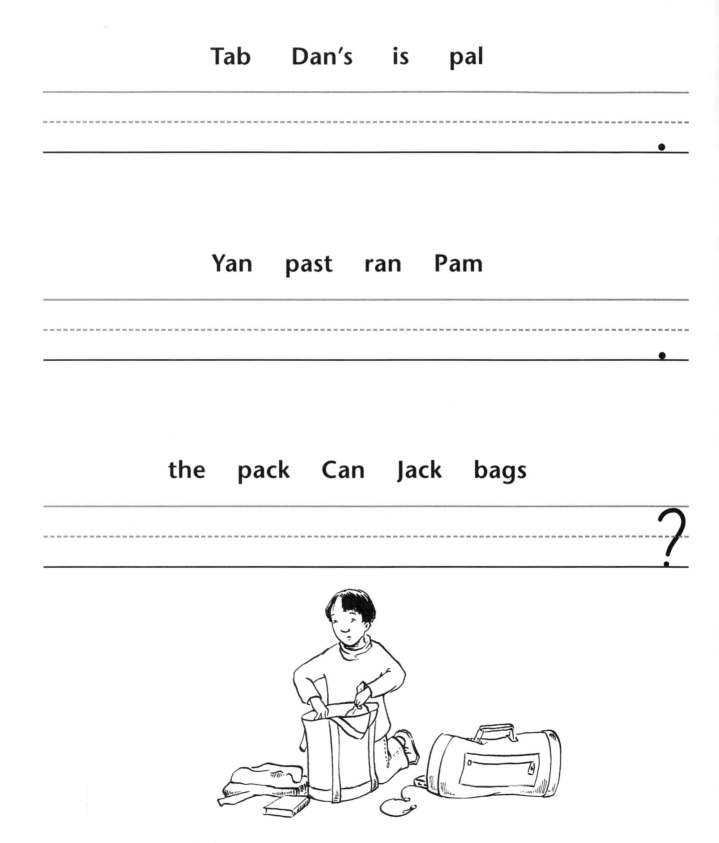

## Lesson 3: Short Vowel i

Vowels are **short** when there is **one vowel** followed by **only consonants**.

pin

Sound out the letters to read each word.

| it | hit | him | pin |
| big | did | dig | pig |
| sit | lip | rib | rip |
| six | win | lid | sip |

| mix | sick | fill | slid |
| mitt | lick | dim | miss |
| rim | kit | wig | kid |
| fix | kill | pill | dip |

Learn to read these words: **yes  no    I  you    said**

➜ Circle the word that does **not** rhyme.

| **hit** | it | bit | wig | sit | pit |
| **win** | fin | din | bin | pin | pill |
| **lip** | dip | nip | hip | rim | sip |

→ Circle the name of the picture.

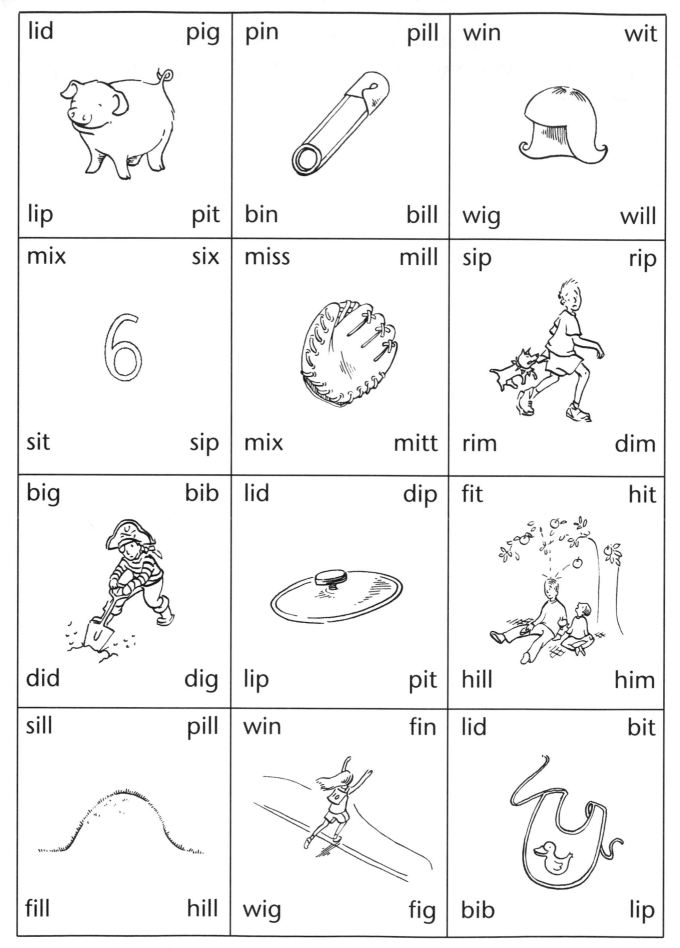

| | |
|---|---|
| lid · pig | pin · pill |
| lip · pit | bin · bill |

| win · wit |
|---|
| wig · will |

| mix · six | miss · mill | sip · rip |
|---|---|---|
| sit · sip | mix · mitt | rim · dim |

| big · bib | lid · dip | fit · hit |
|---|---|---|
| did · dig | lip · pit | hill · him |

| sill · pill | win · fin | lid · bit |
|---|---|---|
| fill · hill | wig · fig | bib · lip |

➜ Circle the name of the picture.

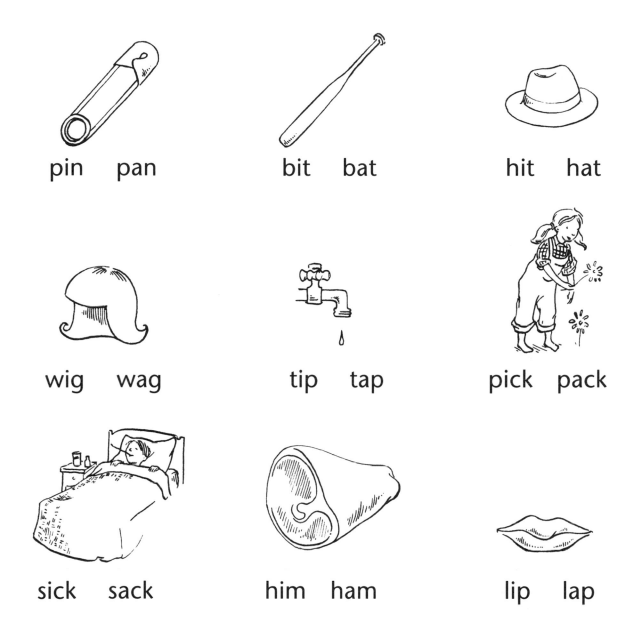

pin    pan          bit    bat          hit    hat

wig    wag          tip    tap          pick    pack

sick    sack          him    ham          lip    lap

➜ Change the short **a** to short **i** and write it on the line. Then read the new word.

sat   s___t      lad   l___d      bat   b___t      Max   m___x

fan   f___n      dam   d___m      bag   b___g      rap   r___p

→ Read the sentence and circle the missing word. Then write the word on the line.

1. Rick's dad has _____ pigs          sip          six          fix

   and a rab-bit.

2. The rat _____ the man's hand.      bib          big          bit

3. I will _____ Kim at camp.          miss         mix          win

4. Will the lid _____ the pan?        hit          fit          kick

5. The cat _____ the rat in           bit          hit          hid

   a tin can.

6. Sam has a _____ in his mitt.       tip          rip          lip

7. Jill and Jan had a ham sal-ad           pit          pick         pic-nic

   at the _____.

8. Can Dad _____ the yams             mitt         fit          fix

   in the pan?

→ Circle the correct answer.

1. Can a man sit in a cab?      **yes**   **no**

2. Can a pin fix a rip?      **yes**   **no**

3. Can a bat hit?      **yes**   **no**

4. Can a lip kick?      **yes**   **no**

5. Can lips kiss?      **yes**   **no**

6. Can a cat lick?      **yes**   **no**

7. Is a pig a ham?      **yes**   **no**

8. Is a map in an at-las?      **yes**   **no**

# The Din-Lin

📖 Read the story.

     A Din-Lin is as big as an ant. It has 2 backs, 3 hips, 6 hands, and 4 lips.

Draw the Din-Lin.

➔ Circle the correct answer.

1. A Din-Lin is as big as  (a) a rat  (b) an ant  (c) a rab-bit

2. A Din-Lin has ____ hands.  (a) 2  (b) 4  (c) 6

3. A Din-Lin has ____ lips.  (a)  2  (b) 4  (c) 6

✎ Write a story with the words. Then read the story to see that it makes sense.

**his     Jim     lip     bit**

_____

**The     hand     licks     Kim's     cat**

_____

**fast     pigs     Six     pink     ran**

_____

# The Cat and the Rats

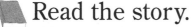 Read the story.

Mr. and Mrs. Rat had six kids: Bill, Will, Jill, Sam, Tam, and Pam.

"Max, the big cat, will grab the kids," said Mrs. Rat.

Did Max grab Bill, Will, Jill, Sam, Tam, and Pam?

No, Mr. and Mrs. Rat hid the kids in the at-tic.

➜ Circle the correct answer.

1. Mr. and Mrs. Rat had _____ kids.  (a) 3  (b) 5  (c) 6

2. The cat is   (a) Will  (b) Max  (c) Tam

3. Mrs. Rat said the cat will _____ the kids.
   (a) lick  (b) nip  (c) grab

4. The kids hid in   (a) a pit  (b) a pan  (c) an at-tic

✎ Write a story with the words. Then read the story to see that it makes sense.

big    is    and    Sid    fit

_____

_____

_____ •

kid    Jill    Mrs.    Rat's    is

_____

_____

_____ •

pan    the    in    big    hid    Tim

_____

_____

_____ •

# Twin Rab-bits

    Yin had twin rab-bits, Sam and Sim. Sam was sick. Sam had a sip of milk and a pill. Sam sat in Yin's hat and had a nap.

    Sim was not sick. He was fit. He had a big bit of ham and a glass of milk.

    Sim was sad. "I miss Sam," he said. "I can't fit in Yin's hat. I will nap in Kitt's mitt."

    And he did. He had a nap in it.

➔ Circle the correct answer.

1. Twin rab-bits = _____ rab-bits.  (a) 1  (b) 2  (c) 3

2. Sam was   (a) sad  (b) mad  (c) sick

3. Sam had   (a) ham  (b) milk  (c) jam

4. Sim
   (a) sat in a hat  (b) was sick  (c) had a nap in Kitt's mitt

✎ Write a story with the words. Then read the story to see that it makes sense.

said    fit    Sim    was    he

_____

- - - - - - - - - - - - - - - - - - - - - - - - - -

_____

- - - - - - - - - - - - - - - - - - - - - - - - - -

_____●

Rick's    had    pants    rip    a

_____

- - - - - - - - - - - - - - - - - - - - - - - - - -

_____

- - - - - - - - - - - - - - - - - - - - - - - - - -

_____●

can    van    a    Six    kids    in    fit

_____

- - - - - - - - - - - - - - - - - - - - - - - - - -

_____

- - - - - - - - - - - - - - - - - - - - - - - - - -

_____●

Vowels are **short** when there is **one vowel** followed by **only consonants**.

dog

Sound out the letters to read each word.

| on | not | hop | nod |
|----|-----|-----|-----|
| top | pot | box | hot |
| dog | mop | lot | jog |
| job | pop | dot | Mom |

| sob | log | got | fox |
|-----|-----|-----|-----|
| cop | rod | rock | rob |
| sock | doll | pop | lock |
| Tom | toss | loss | pod |

Learn to read these words:   **of    to    they**

→ Draw a line between the words that rhyme.

| jog | cob | fox | cod | Don | dock |
|-----|-----|-----|-----|-----|------|
| Bob | log | nod | ox | lock | Ron |
| pan | tan | sick | rock | rim | pot |
| pop | top | sock | Rick | lot | Tim |

→ Circle the name of the picture.

| pot          Bob | rot          cob | top          pod |
|---|---|---|
| ox          box | rob          cop | dot          pot |
| lock          sock | log          rod | rob          rod |
| rock          dock | lot          sob | cod          cob |
| pod          top | dot          dog | rob          rock |
| pop          job | dock          doll | rot          lock |
| hot          hit | sock          lick | rat          hot |
| hop          hip | sack          lock | rot          dog |

→ Write in the missing letter. Then read the word.

| | b | | d | | t |
|---|---|---|---|---|---|
| ho__ | t | to__ | x | mo__ | r |
| | l | | p | | m |
| | b | | d | | z |
| jo__ | m | do__ | g | bo__ | x |
| | s | | p | | t |

→ Write in the missing letter. Then read the sentence to see that it makes sense.

1. Tom and Tim sat on a _____ock.          s    l    r

2. Mom got a _____ob.                       p    n    j

3. The top of the pot was _____ot.          n    h    t

4. Todd will fix Ann's _____ocks.           s    b    l

5. Dot had a _____og.                       t    d    p

6. Will the big _____oll fit into the box?  d    b    l

→ Read the words below. Then choose a word to complete each sentence. Write the word on the line.

lock          rock          dog          jogging

1. Dad is hot from _____.

2. Will Deb toss the _____ into the pond?

3. Bob is sad. He has lost his _____.

4. "Can you fix this _____?" she asked.

socks          box          pot          log

5. The big ham will not fit into the _____.

6. Jan's doll is in the _____.

7. Rick has a lot of _____.

8. Ron sat on a _____ and had his pic-nic.

➔ Put an X in the box next to the sentence that tells about the picture.

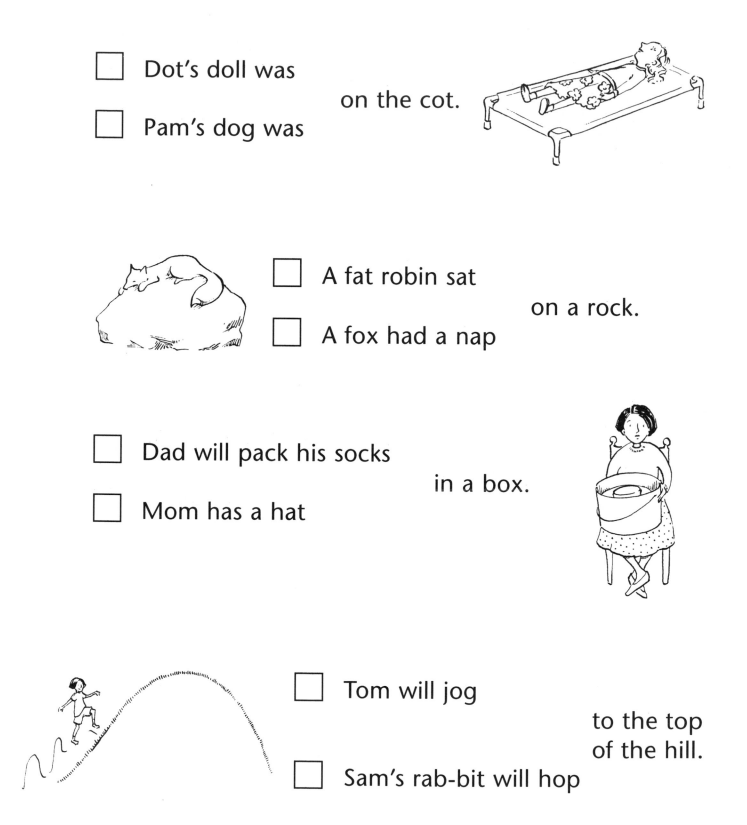

☐ Dot's doll was

☐ Pam's dog was

on the cot.

☐ A fat robin sat

☐ A fox had a nap

on a rock.

☐ Dad will pack his socks

☐ Mom has a hat

in a box.

☐ Tom will jog

☐ Sam's rab-bit will hop

to the top
of the hill.

# At the Hos-pi-tal

Read the story. Then number the pictures in the order they come in the story.

_____          _____          _____

Ann is sick. Mom vis-its Ann in the hos-pit-al. Mom has a rag doll in a box. Ann rocks the doll. Ann has a nap and the doll has a nap in the box.

→ Circle the correct answer.

1. Ann is   (a) sad  (b) sick  (c) hot

2. (a) Mom  (b) Dad  (b) Ann   visits the hos-pi-tal

3. Ann   (a) rocks  (b) hits  (c) rips       the doll

4. Ann and the doll   (a) sit  (b) sob  (c) nap

✎ Write a story with the words. Then read the story to see that it makes sense.

a   has   doll   rag   Ann

_____

_____

_____  •


Don   socks   his   lost

_____

_____

_____  •


The   pond   hop   will   frog   the   into

_____

_____

_____  •

# Mr. Dodd and the Rob-in

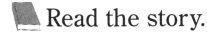 Read the story.

Mr. Dodd sits on a log on the top of the hill. Mr. Dodd has a big box.

"You can hop into the box and nap," said Mr. Dodd to Rob, the rob-in.

"You can-not trick rob-ins," said Rob, the rob-in. "I will not nap in the box."

"It is hot. You can sit in the box. It is not hot in the box," said Mr. Dodd to Rab, the rab-bit.

"You can-not trick rab-bits," said Rab, the rab-bit. "I will not sit in the box."

"A ham is in the box," Mr. Dodd said to Rat, the rat. "You can get a bit if you hop into the box."

"You can-not trick rats," said Rat. "I will not hop into the box."

No an-i-mal got into the box, and Mr. Dodd was mad.

→ Circle the correct answer.

1. Mr. Dodd is a   (a) rab-bit  (b) rat  (c) fox

2. Mr. Dodd has a   (a) pot  (b) pit  (c) box

3. Rab, the rab-bit, said, "I will not
    (a) sit  (b) hop  (c) nap

4. Mr. Dodd is   (a) sad  (b) mad  (c) sick

✎ Write a story with the words. Then read the story to see that it makes sense.

**animals    Mr.    Dodd    Did    the    trick**

_____

- - - - - - - - - - - - - - - - - - - - - - - - - - - -

_____

_____ ?

- - - - - - - - - - - - - - - - - - - - - - - - - - - -

_____

**the    the    hill    top    Bob    to    got    of**

_____

- - - - - - - - - - - - - - - - - - - - - - - - - - - -

_____

_____

- - - - - - - - - - - - - - - - - - - - - - - - - - - -

_____ •

**hot    from    got    Dot    jogging**

_____

- - - - - - - - - - - - - - - - - - - - - - - - - - - -

_____

_____

- - - - - - - - - - - - - - - - - - - - - - - - - - - -

_____ •

## Lesson 5: Short Vowel u

Vowels are **short** when there is **one vowel** followed by **only consonants**.

cup

Sound out the letters to read each word.

| | | | |
|---|---|---|---|
| up | us | fun | sun |
| bus | sun | mud | jug |
| run | cut | bun | hum |
| tug | rub | nut | bug |

| | | | |
|---|---|---|---|
| cub | duck | mug | fuss |
| dug | cuff | pup | dull |
| but | tub | gun | buzz |
| luck | rug | bud | hug |

Learn to read these words:   **put**   **pull**   **full**   **bull**

➜ Circle the word that does **not** rhyme.

| **bug** | jug | mug | tub | hug | dug |
|---|---|---|---|---|---|
| **cut** | nut | rut | hut | mud | but |
| **sun** | fun | bun | ran | run | gun |

→ Circle the name of the picture.

| | | |
|---|---|---|
| cup     bug<br><br>pup     rug | hut     bus<br><br>but     bud | cuff     fuss<br><br>cub     buzz |
| cup     tug<br><br>mug     jug | luck     dull<br><br>duck     dug | nap     nuts<br><br>not     huts |
| put     full<br><br>pull     bull | run     ram<br><br>rum     rim | bag     big<br><br>bug     but |
| tug     bud<br><br>mud     bad | sock     sum<br><br>sack     sun | top     tug<br><br>tip     tub |

➜ Add a short **u** to find the name of each picture. Write the number of the picture in the box.

☐ c __ p

☐ b __ n

☐ r __ g

☐ s __ m

☐ c __ t

☐ h __ g

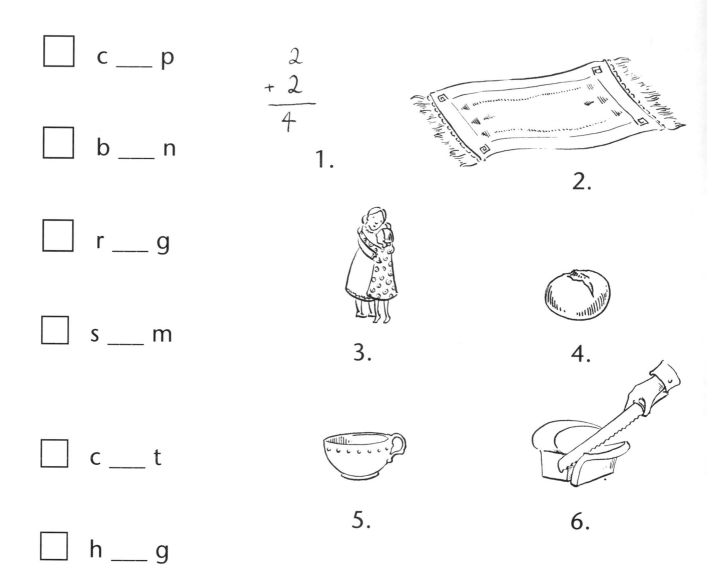

$$\begin{array}{r} 2 \\ +\ 2 \\ \hline 4 \end{array}$$

1.

2.

3.

4.

5.

6.

➜ Add two new vowels to make two new words. Read the new words.

| luck | l __ ck | l __ ck |
| cut | c __ t | c __ t |
| hum | h __ m | h __ m |
| dug | d __ g | d __ g |

→ Read the sentence and circle the missing word. Write the word on the line. Then read the sentence to see that it makes sense.

1. The dog had _____ in the mud.          fun     run     tub

2. The _____ got up on Ann's lap.          bug     bull    pup

3. Dad hid Jus-tin's _____.          hut     hum     gum

4. Mom and Gus sat in the _____.          mud     sun     jug

5. A duck can-not _____ fast.          rub     run     hum

6. A _____ got into the jug.          duck    pup     bug

7. Tom's cat had a nap on the _____.          jug     tub     rug

8. The kids got on the _____.          rug     bun     bus

→ Circle the correct answer.

1. Can you cut a bud?     **yes   no**

2. Can you fill a jug?     **yes   no**

3. Can the sun run?     **yes   no**

4. Can you suck gum?     **yes   no**

5. Can you put a cub in a mug?     **yes   no**

6. Can a duck hum?     **yes   no**

7. Can you pick up a rug?     **yes   no**

8. Can you sit in a tub?     **yes   no**

# Bud the Pup

📘 Read the story.

Dad got Bud a pup. It is full of fun. It tugs at the rug, runs in the sun, and digs in the mud. It puts Bud's sock in the tub and rips his cap.

But Bud is not mad. Bud hugs his pup and it jumps up on his lap and licks his hand.

➔ Circle the correct answer.

1. Bud got   (a) a duck  (b) a cub  (c) a pup

2. The pup rips  (a) Mom's hat  (b) Dad's cap  (c) Bud's cap

3. The pup puts Bud's socks
   (a) in the sun  (b) in the mud   (c) in the tub

4. Bud is  (a) mad  (b) not mad  (c) full of fun

5. The pup  (a) bit Bud's hand
   (b) licks Bud's hand  (c) cuts Bud's hand

✎ Write a story with the words. Then read the story to see that it makes sense.

of   is   fun   pup   Bud's   full

_____

- - - - - - - - - - - - - - - - - - - - - - - - - - -

_____

- - - - - - - - - - - - - - - - - - - - - - - - - - -

_____•___

*Challenge

hop   A   bug   can   but   duck   a   can-not

_____

- - - - - - - - - - - - - - - - - - - - - - - - - - -

_____

- - - - - - - - - - - - - - - - - - - - - - - - - - -

_____•___

# Tom Vis-its Dr. Kung

📖 Read the story.

Tom had to vis-it Dr. Kung at 1:00 p.m.

"You must run," Dad said to Mom. "You will miss the bus."

Huff, puff, Mom and Tom ran up the hill and got to the bus stop just as the bus got to the stop. But the bus did not stop.

"It is full," said a man at the stop. He was mad and got a cab.

"Hop in," the man said to Mom and Tom. "The cab is fast. It will pass the bus."

Mom and Tom got in. The cab did pass the bus and they got to Dr. Kung's just at 1:00 p.m.

➜ Circle the correct answer.

1. Tom had to vis-it
   (a) Mr. Kung  (b) Dr. Kung  (c) Ms. Kung

2. Tom and Mom ran
   (a) past the pond  (b) past the bus  (c) up the hill

3. A ____ got a cab.  (a) Mom  (b) man  (c) Tom

4. Mom and Tom  (a) ran back to Dad  (b) got to
   Dr. Kung's at 1:00 p.m.  (c) did not get to Dr. Kung's

✎ Write a story with the words. Then read the story to see that it makes sense.

**get    and    not    Tom    the    Mom    did    bus**

_____

- - - - - - - - - - - - - - - - - - - - - - - - - - -

_____

_____

- - - - - - - - - - - - - - - - - - - - - - - - - - -

_____ •

**the    fun    dig    is    to    in    It    mud**

_____

- - - - - - - - - - - - - - - - - - - - - - - - - - -

_____

_____

- - - - - - - - - - - - - - - - - - - - - - - - - - -

_____ •

*Challenge

**ham    the    Dad    cut    and    bun    in    a    it    put**

_____

- - - - - - - - - - - - - - - - - - - - - - - - - - -

_____

_____

- - - - - - - - - - - - - - - - - - - - - - - - - - -

_____ •

## Lesson 6: Short Vowel e

Vowels are **short** when there is **one vowel** followed by **only consonants**.

egg

Sound out the letters to read each word.

| | | | |
|---|---|---|---|
| bed | leg | yes | get |
| pen | men | red | beg |
| yet | ten | wed | wet |
| Ted | jet | fed | den |

| | | | |
|---|---|---|---|
| yell | less | hem | neck |
| set | Ben | mess | well |
| led | sell | bet | desk |
| fell | egg | peck | tell |

Learn to read these words:  he  she  we  me  be
were  there

→ Draw a line between the words that rhyme.

| | | | | | |
|---|---|---|---|---|---|
| bell | tell | mess | ten | red | get |
| egg | leg | men | less | pet | Ted |
| tin | bug | peg | bag | dock | luck |
| hug | win | rag | beg | duck | lock |

➔ Circle the name of the picture.

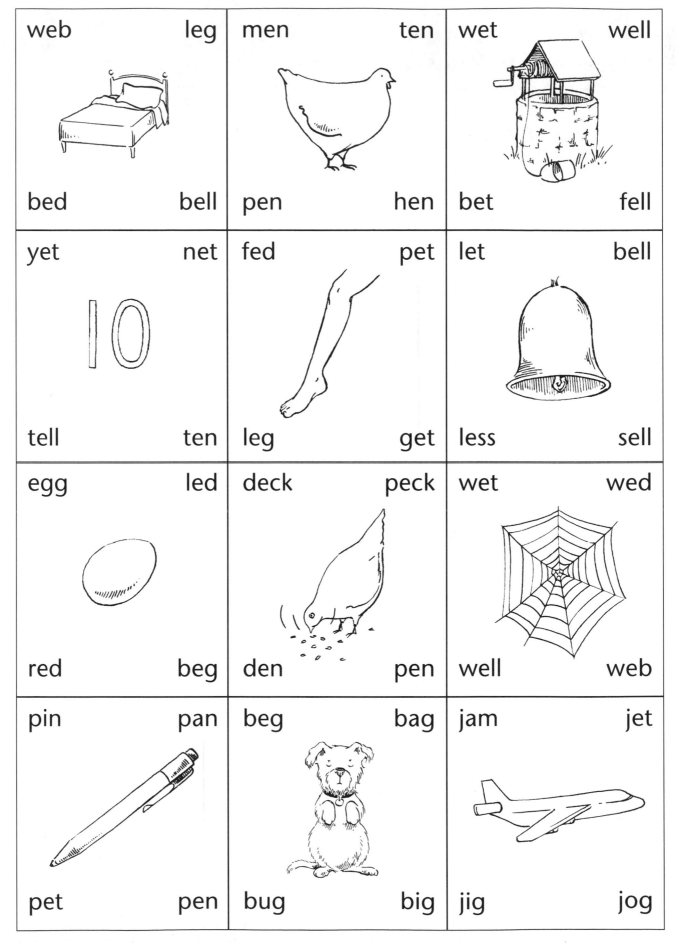

| web      leg | men      ten | wet      well |
|--------------|--------------|---------------|
| bed      bell | pen      hen | bet      fell |
| yet      net | fed      pet | let      bell |
| tell      ten | leg      get | less      sell |
| egg      led | deck      peck | wet      wed |
| red      beg | den      pen | well      web |
| pin      pan | beg      bag | jam      jet |
| pet      pen | bug      big | jig      jog |

➜ Read the words. Then circle the short **e** words.

|        |        |        |
|--------|--------|--------|
| big    | pin    | rid    |
| bug    | pen    | rod    |
| beg    | pan    | red    |

|        |        |
|--------|--------|
| tin    | deck   |
| ten    | dock   |
| tan    | duck   |

|        |        |        |
|--------|--------|--------|
| lid    | din    | hum    |
| led    | Dan    | hem    |
| lad    | den    | ham    |

➜ Write in the missing letter. Then read the sentence to see that it makes sense.

1. Jeff will ___ell the hen's ten eggs.          t    l    s

2. "Nesim, can you lend Ben a ___en?"          g    p    d

3. The men ___ed the pigs in the pen.          r    j    f

4. Bev's pup fell into the well and got ___et.          w    m    y

5. "I ___et you ten bits of gum I will win,"          t    b    k
said Len.

6. "You must not ___ell. Dad is in bed,"          x    y    z
Mom said.

→ Read the sentence and circle the missing word. Then write the word on the line.

1. Ned has one _____ and ten ducks.

leg      den      hen

2. "I can tell you are not _____," said Mom.

yell      well      fell

3. Ken _____ and cut his leg.

fed      fell      tell

4. Bev had ham, an _____, and a bun.

jet      neck      egg

5. Ted's pet dog can sit up and _____.

bat      bet      beg

6. The _____ rang and the kids ran into class.

bill      bell      bull

7. The ten men _____ on the jet.

wet      went      well

8. Bet-tina had to get her pet rab-bit to the _____.

vet      jet      den

→ Put an X in the box next to the sentence that tells about the picture.

☐ "Ed, will you get a wet rag and mop up this mess?"

☐ "Nell, can you fix Pam's hem?"

☐ "Has Dad fed the pigs yet?"

☐ "Can you tell me if there is a bus at six p.m.?"

☐ "I bet you cannot run up the hill as fast as I can."

☐ "I bet I can yell as well as Peg can."

☐ "Is the cub in its den?"

☐ "Is a bug in the web?"

| **Ed** has the sound of **ed only** when it follows **d** or **t**. Other times it has the sound of **d** or **t**. | **ed** | land-ed, hunt-ed |
| | **d** | pulled, tugged |
| | **t** | tripped, asked |

## The Leg Men

 Read the story. Circle the **ed** words and make sure you read them correctly.

Ben was in the den. He tripped on the rug and fell and fell . . . and fell . . . until he land-ed in a big web.

"Help! Help!" he yelled. "Help!"

He yelled and yelled, and he pulled and tugged at the web un-til at last he said, "I quit."

As he fell back into the web, ten men ran up. They ran well as they had six legs! They had six legs, and they had 4 hands. But they had no necks.

"Help me! Help me!" begged Ben.

"Yes, we will help you," said the leg men. "We must be fast as the web is the drag-on's and he will kid-nap you."

They pulled and tugged Ben. At last, he fell . . . onto the rug in the den.

He sat up on the rug just as his mom ran in. "Are you OK?" she asked.

"Yes, I'm OK," Ben said. "But if the leg men had not helped me . . . ."

"The leg men?" Mom asked.

"Yes, the leg men pulled me from the web."

"The web?" Mom said. "Leg men and webs! Well, I'm glad the leg men helped you. Let's get you to bed!"

→ Now re-read the story and circle the correct answer.

1. Ben landed in   (a) a pen   (b) a web   (c) a net

2. (a) 2   (b) 6   (c) 10     men helped Ben.

3. The men had _____ legs.   (a) 2   (b) 6   (c) 10

4. The men   (a) yelled at Ben
   (b) tugged and pulled Ben   (c) kid-napped Ben

5. At the end, Ben land-ed   (a) back in the web
   (b) in the drag-on's den     (c) on the den rug

6. At the end, Mom was   (a) mad   (b) glad   (c) sad

✎ Write a story with the words. Then read the story to see that it makes sense.

**and    Ben    rug    fell    tripped    the    on**

_____

- - - - - - - - - - - - - - - - - - - - - - - - - -

_____

_____

- - - - - - - - - - - - - - - - - - - - - - - - - -

_____ •

**the    and    got    pond    fell    wet    Meg    in**

_____

- - - - - - - - - - - - - - - - - - - - - - - - - -

_____

_____

- - - - - - - - - - - - - - - - - - - - - - - - - -

_____ •

**slept    Ned    went    well    bed    to    and**

_____

- - - - - - - - - - - - - - - - - - - - - - - - - -

_____

_____

- - - - - - - - - - - - - - - - - - - - - - - - - -

_____ •

## Lesson 7: Review of Short Vowels

| short vowels | a    e    i    o    u |
|---|---|

➜ Circle the words that do **not** have the vowel.

| a | big | bag | bed | but | bat |
|---|---|---|---|---|---|
| i | lid | lot | sip | set | bet |
| o | hem | hot | hat | him | hut |
| u | cup | wet | ran | tub | nod |
| e | top | ten | egg | rug | rim |

➜ Use two letters from each word to make new words. Write the words on the lines. The first one is done for you.

1. bed     **fed**     **bad**     **be**t

2. pit     s____     ____o____     ____g

3. hot     n____     ____i____     ____p

4. rag     b____     ____u____     ____n

5. map     t____     ____o____     ____t

6. but     h____     ____e____     ____s

→ Draw a line to the correct ending of the sentence.

1. Jill fell and tipped     his red mug.

2. Ken put the ham     the full jug.

3. Max filled up     into the hot pan.

4. Nan has     on a jet to Hol-land.

5. Mom went     a van from Jap-an.

6. Jed got     a pen pal in Fin-land.

7. Liz's pup let the kids     and got lost.

8. Bob's cat got up on his lap     pat and hug him.

9. Pam's pet rab-bit hopped from its pen     and licked him.

→ Choose a word from the list to complete each sentence. Then write the word on the line. Read the sentence to see that it makes sense.

1. Pat will sell his red van and get a _____ van.    job

2. Jack _____ in the pond and got wet.    hid

3. The _____ bit Mac on the neck.    fell

4. Mom gets the bus to get to her_____.    black

5. The red hen _____ the eggs in the big box.    bug

6. They got _____ from the pic-nic at sun-set.    put

7. Peg will _____ as she is fast.    back

8. Nick lost his _____ tick-et in the mix-up.    bus

9. Emil dressed up his kit-ten and _____ him in the doll's cot.    sick

10. Kim was _____ but she is back in class.    win

# Rick

Read the story. Then number the pictures in the order they come in the story.

Learn to read this word:    **then**

Rick's mom has a job and he has no Dad. Rick gets himself up.

He pulls back the blan-kets on his bed. Rick gets into a tub. **Then** he gets his jacket and pants from the closet and puts them on.

Next, he gets him-self a muf-fin and a cup of milk. **Then** he locks up and gets the bus.

He gets back at 3:30 p.m. He tells his mom he is back. **Then** he puts on his jogging pants and top.

Next, he has a snack. **Then** he mops, dusts, and picks up un-til Mom gets back at 5:00 p.m.

She tells Rick he is a big help.

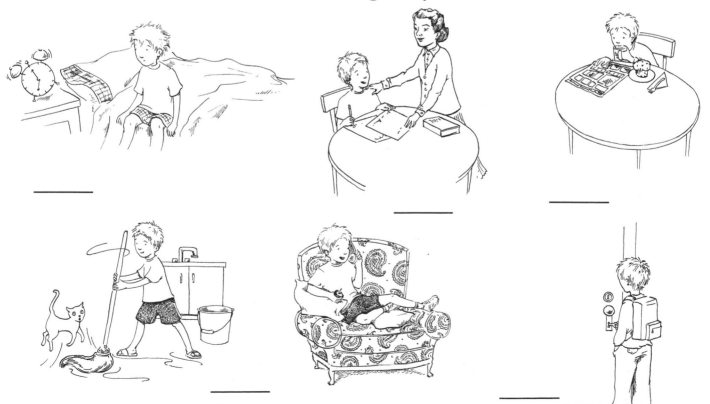

✏️ Write a story with the words. Then read the story. Check to see that it makes sense.

**job   Mom   a   at   has   bank   Rick's   a**

_____

- - - - - - - - - - - - - - - - - - - - - - - - - -

_____

- - - - - - - - - - - - - - - - - - - - - - - - - -

_____ •

**hen's   nest   There   eggs   were   red   the   in   ten**

- - - - - - - - - - - - - - - - - - - - - - - - - -

_____

- - - - - - - - - - - - - - - - - - - - - - - - - -

_____

- - - - - - - - - - - - - - - - - - - - - - - - - -

_____

- - - - - - - - - - - - - - - - - - - - - - - - - -

_____ •

**rip   fix   in   will   jack-et   Todd   his   the**

- - - - - - - - - - - - - - - - - - - - - - - - - -

_____

- - - - - - - - - - - - - - - - - - - - - - - - - -

_____

- - - - - - - - - - - - - - - - - - - - - - - - - -

_____ •

# Anil and His Ox

 Read the story.

Learn to read this word:  **story**

A **story** can tell a les-son. Can you tell the les-son in this story from In-di-a?

Anil had a big, strong ox.

"The ox can pull ten wag-ons," Anil said to his pal, Ram.

"The ox can-not pull ten wag-ons," said Ram.

"Yes, he can," Anil said.

"I bet you ten ducks, sev-en hens, and six pigs, the ox can-not pull the wag-ons," said Ram.

"And I bet you ten ducks, sev-en hens, and six pigs he can," said Anil.

They got the wag-ons and Anil hit the ox and said, "Get up, you bad an-i-mal. Get a-long, you ras-cal. Pull the wag-ons."

But the ox did not pull the wag-ons.

"Get up! Get a-long, you ras-cal!" yelled Anil, hit-ting the ox.

But the ox still did not pull the wag-ons.

At last, Anil stopped yell-ing at the ox and hit-ting him. He was mad. He had lost his bet.

He led the ox back to his pen. Then the ox said to him, "It is bad to hit me, yell at me, and tell me I am a ras-cal. You are a bad man."

"Yes, I am a bad man," said Anil. "I will stop hit-ting you and tell-ing you you are a ras-cal."

"If you stop, I will pull the wag-ons," the ox said.

Anil hugged and pat-ted the ox. Then he fed him well and led him back to his pal Ram.

"I bet you a hun-dred ducks, hens, and pigs the ox can pull the ten wag-ons," Anil said to his pal.

Ram grinned, "And I bet you a hun-dred ducks, hens, and pigs he can-not," he said.

They got the wag-ons. Anil pat-ted the ox and said, "You are the strong-est, best an-i-mal."

The ox be-gan to pull the ten wag-ons. He pulled and pulled, until he pulled the wag-ons up to Anil and Ram.

"Well!" said Ram. "He is the strong-est and best an-i-mal. You win the bet."

Anil pat-ted the ox and fed him.

➔ Circle the correct answer.

To get the ox to pull the wag-ons   (a) Anil hit him
    (b) Anil stopped hit-ting him  (c) Ram hit him

The les-son of the story is: You will not get help un-less

you _____.

✎ Write a story with the words. Then read the story. Check to see that it makes sense.

**man's the an-i-mal strongest ox The best and was**

_____

- - - - - - - - - - - - - - - - - - - - - - - - - - - - - - - -

_____

- - - - - - - - - - - - - - - - - - - - - - - - - - - - - - - -

_____ •

**The went the bus on to mall kids the**

_____

- - - - - - - - - - - - - - - - - - - - - - - - - - - - - - - -

_____

- - - - - - - - - - - - - - - - - - - - - - - - - - - - - - - -

_____ •

**jack-et on black his Rick put**

_____

- - - - - - - - - - - - - - - - - - - - - - - - - - - - - - - -

_____

- - - - - - - - - - - - - - - - - - - - - - - - - - - - - - - -

_____ •

| l blends | bl | cl | fl | gl | pl | sl |
|---|---|---|---|---|---|---|

Sound out the letters to read each word.

**bl**   black   blink   bless

**cl**   class   clap clip

**fl**   flag fled Fred

**gl**   glass   Glen   glad

**pl**   plot plum   plus

**sl**   slid slap sled

| | | | |
|---|---|---|---|
| flat | slim | club | blank |
| cliff | blot | slip | clock |
| slam | glum | plan | blan-ket |

➜ Circle the word with a blend.

| black | back | sunk | sun |
|---|---|---|---|
| gas | glass | slip | sip |
| gum | glum | fled | fed |
| cap | clap | plan | pan |

→ Circle the name of the picture.

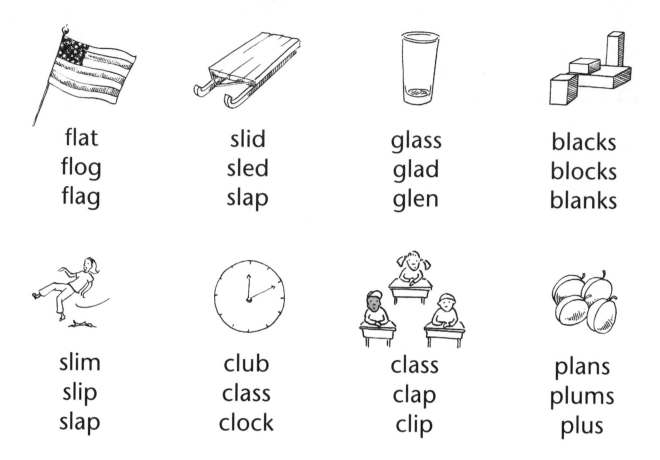

| flat | slid | glass | blacks |
| flog | sled | glad | blocks |
| flag | slap | glen | blanks |

| slim | club | class | plans |
| slip | class | clap | plums |
| slap | clock | clip | plus |

→ Write in the missing blend. Then read the sentence to see that it makes sense.

1. Vas-il pulled the _____ed up the hill.          fl    cl    sl

2. Flip had six _____ack pups.          pl    bl    fl

3. The class _____apped at the end of the story.          sl    cl    gl

4. Bob _____ipped and cut his leg.          bl    pl    sl

5. Mel-ik fed the _____ock of ducks.          bl    cl    fl

6. Glenda had a glass of milk, a bun, and _____um jam.          gl    bl    pl

→ Put an X in the box next to the sentence that tells about the picture.

☐ Todd fell and spilled his glass of milk.

☐ Dad put a flan-nel blan-ket on the bed.

☐ Sal-im jogs and is slim.

☐ Tim is flat on a mat.

☐ The kids got to the top of the cliff.

☐ The class did the sums.

☐ "If you will pick the black plums, I will pick the red plums," said Dad.

☐ "The clock is fast," said Mom.

✎ Write a story with the words. Then read the story. Check to see that it makes sense.

**The   picnic   had   kids   a**

_____

- - - - - - - - - - - - - - - - - - - - - - - - - -

_____


✎ Write a story about the picture. Use at least 3 of the words.

**class   glad   sled   slid**

| r blends | br | cr | dr | fr | gr | pr | tr |
|----------|----|----|----|----|----|----|----|

Sound out the letters to read each word.

| br | brag | brass | brick |
|----|------|-------|-------|
| cr | crab | crack | cross |
| dr | dress | drag | drip |
| fr | frog | Fred | frill |
| gr | grass | grin | grab |
| pr | prick | prop | press |
| tr | trod | trip | trap |

| from | bran | crib | grill |
|------|------|------|-------|
| trim | crop | drop | trick |
| Grand-dad | tram | drum | drag-on |

→ Read the words. Draw a line to the beginning blend.

| truck | cr | frog | pr | drab | gr |
|-------|----|------|----|------|----|
| brick | tr | grab | gr | grin | dr |
| cross | br | press | fr | crack | cr |
| tred | cr | bran | pr | track | pr |
| grill | gr | print | fr | prod | dr |
| crab | tr | frill | br | drop | tr |

➜ Circle the name of the picture.

| | | | |
|---|---|---|---|
| grab | track | grass | track |
| crab | trick | dress | crack |
| brag | brick | drag | brack-et |

| | | | |
|---|---|---|---|
| grill | tram | cross | frog |
| grin | drum | press | frill |
| grass | prim | prick | grill |

➜ Read the sentence and circle the correct word.

1. Dad was mad. The pup (tricked, tracked) mud into the den.

2. "Put the (grass, dress) in the clos-et," said Mom.

3. Grand-dad is slim and (trim, grin) as he jogs.

4. The glass had a (crick, crack) in it.

5. Meg (trapped, tripped) on a crab in the sand.

6. They had the pic-nic on a blan-ket on the (glass, grass).

# Fred and Fran

Read the story. Then write the number of the sentence that tells about each picture.

**1.** Mom got Fred a jack-et and Fran a dress.

**2.** Fred and Fran un-packed the jack-et and dress. The jack-et was red and had big but-tons. The dress was plum and had frills at the top and bot-tom.

**3.** Fred put on the jack-et and Fran put on the dress. "The jack-et fits well," grinned Fred. "The dress is the best. It's as grand as can be," bragged Fran.

**4.** Fran ran into the den. Grand-dad was there. She tripped and ripped the hem of the dress.

_____

**5.** "Bad luck," said Grand-dad, as Fran got up. "But it's OK. I can fix the hem. Get the pins and I will pin it up." Fran got the pins and Grand-dad fixed the hem.

_____

_____

_____

✎ Write a story with the words. Then read the story. Check to see that it makes sense.

**Fran's    Grand-dad    fixed    hem**

_____

- - - - - - - - - - - - - - - - - - - - - - - - - - - - - - - - - - - - - - - - - - - -

_____ •

✎ Write a story about the picture. Use at least 3 of these words.

**frog    grass    grab    track    trick    grin**

_____

- - - - - - - - - - - - - - - - - - - - - - - - - - - - - - - - - - - - - - - - - - - -

_____

- - - - - - - - - - - - - - - - - - - - - - - - - - - - - - - - - - - - - - - - - - - -

_____

- - - - - - - - - - - - - - - - - - - - - - - - - - - - - - - - - - - - - - - - - - - -

_____

## Lesson 10: Beginning Blends with s

| s blends | sc | sk | sm | sn | sp | st | sw |
|----------|----|----|----|----|----|----|----|

Sound out the letters to read each word.

| | | | |
|-----|--------|--------|--------|
| **sc** | Scott | scrub | scan |
| **sk** | skin | skull | skip |
| **sm** | smell | smack | smog |
| **sn** | snack | snip | snug |
| **sp** | spot | sped | spill |
| **st** | step | stop | stem |
| **sw** | swim | swing | swam |

| | | | |
|-------|-------|-------|-------|
| still | spin | snap | swell |
| snag | stack | spit | skim |
| spell | smug | Swiss | stick |

Learn to read these words:  **scratch   split   sprig   strip**

➜ Read the words and circle the blends. Then draw a line between the words that begin with the same blend.

| | | | |
|---|---|---|---|
| spill | snap | swam | smug |
| sniff | spot | twig | swell |
| stop | still | smell | twist |
| scab | Scott | spun | speck |
| skill | skim | strap | sprint |
| stuck | step | sprig | strip |

➜ Circle the name of the picture.

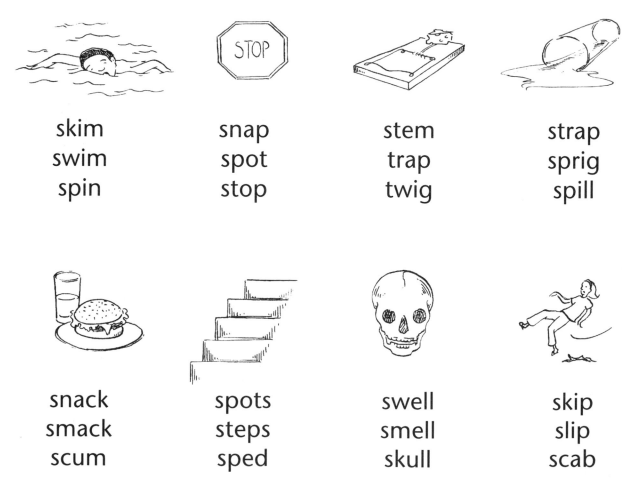

skim
swim
spin

snap
spot
stop

stem
trap
twig

strap
sprig
spill

snack
smack
scum

spots
steps
sped

swell
smell
skull

skip
slip
scab

→ Write in the missing blend. Then read the sentence to see that it makes sense.

sc   sk   sl

sn   sp   st

1. The clock had _____opped at ten p.m.

2. "Sit still!" _____apped Ms. Swin-ton.

3. "Skip, can you _____ell 'splen-did'?" asked Mr. Stop-man.

4. The bus _____idd-ed and got stuck in the mud.

5. Mom got a snack and fed the scraps to _____ott's pup.

6. Jack _____ipped on the wet steps.

# Skip Is Fit, Fit, Fit!

Read the story and circle the s blends.

sc  sk  sl

sn  sp  st

Learn to read these words:  **does   her**

Skip is into fitness. At six a.m. she gets up from **her** snug bed. She **does** 20 sit-ups. At 8:00 a.m. she runs. Then she skips on the spot to stop **her** legs from stif-fen-ing up. She has a hot tub. Next, she grabs a quick snack of a glass of milk and a muf-fin, and runs to **her** job.

At 5:00 p.m. she sprints back. Then she has a swim. She swims 50 laps. Skip can-not stop! At 9:30 p.m. she is back to skip-ping and sit-ups. At 10:00 p.m. she gets in bed. She pulls up the blan-kets and, at last, is still!

→ Re-read the story and circle the correct answer.

1. Skip does not  (a) run  (b) swim  (c) sing

2. Skip does  (a) 2  (b) 12  (c) 20 sit-ups

3. At 8:00 a.m. Skip  (a) runs  (b) has a snack
   (c) has a swim

4. Skip has a snack of  (a) milk and a muf-fin
   (b) ham and eggs  (c) pizza

5. Skip is in bed at  (a) 8:00 a.m.  (b) 9:30 p.m.
   (c) 10:00 p.m.

6. Skip is  (a) big  (b) fit  (c) mad

✎ Write a story with the words. Then read the story. Check to see that it makes sense.

**up    six a.m.    gets    at    Skip**

_____

- - - - - - - - - - - - - - - - - - - - - - -

_____•

**ten p.m.    bed    She    at    in    is**

_____

- - - - - - - - - - - - - - - - - - - - - - -

_____•

✎ Write about 4 things that Skip does to keep fit. Check to see that your sentences make sense.

_____

- - - - - - - - - - - - - - - - - - - - - - -

_____

_____

- - - - - - - - - - - - - - - - - - - - - - -

_____

_____

- - - - - - - - - - - - - - - - - - - - - - -

_____

# Twig Gets a Snack

Read the story and circle the **s** blends.

sc    sk    sl

sn    sp    st

Sniff! Sniff! Sniff! Twig smelled the clams Dad had just scrubbed, split, and put into a pan.

"If I stand up on my back legs I can get a clam," Twig said to her-self.

She jumped up and just as she got a clam, Dad spot-ted her. Was he mad! "Scram! Scram!" he yelled, clap-ping his hands.

Twig sped off. She skid-ded on the mat and slid into a stack of pots and pans. Next, she stepped on Dad's snack and spilled his glass of milk. Then she tripped and land-ed smack in a pan of red plums Dad was can-ning. Was he a mess!

Dad stopped be-ing mad and grinned. He pulled Twig from the pan and said, "Well, Twig, you did get a les-son. I bet it will stop you from snack-ing!"

→ Re-read the story and circle the correct answer.

1. Twig smelled  (a) a ham  (b) clams  (c) yams

2. Twig spilled  (a) a pan of clams  (b) a pan of plums
                  (c) a glass of milk

3. Twig fell into  (a) a pan of clams  (b) a pan of plums
                   (c) a glass of milk

4. Dad  (a) grinned  (b) smacked Twig  (c) scrubbed Twig

5. Twig is  (a) a frog  (b) a drag-on  (c) a cat

✎ Write a story with the words. Then read the story. Check to see that it makes sense.

**jumped    get   clam   Twig   up   to   a**

_____

_____

_____

✎ Write about what happened to Twig after Dad yelled at her.

_____

_____

_____

_____

_____

## Lesson 11: End Blends

| end blends | lf | lp | mp | nd | nk | nt | ng |
|---|---|---|---|---|---|---|---|

Sound out the letters to read each word.

| **lf** | elf | gulf | golf |
|---|---|---|---|
| **lp** | help | gulp | yelp |
| **mp** | camp | limp | jump |
| **nd** | hand | send | pond |
| **nk** | pink | bank | sunk |
| **nt** | hunt | lent | plant |

**ng**    bang    rang    sang    long    song    strong

    ring    sing    wing    rung    sung    stung

| dent | stamp | blend | hint |
|---|---|---|---|
| flung | self | wink | bump |
| stand | sink | rent | blank |

➜ Circle the word with a blend.

| | | | |
|---|---|---|---|
| pan | pant | sunk | sun |
| tint | tin | led | lend |
| hand | had | long | log |
| run | rung | pin | pink |

→ Draw a line between each word and the blend the word **ends** with.

help

elf          **nd     nk**          band

**lf      lp      mp**

lamp          **nt     ng**          sink

sing          pant

→ Read the sentence and circle the missing word. Then write the word on the line.

1. The man sang a long, dull         sing    sang    song
   _____, but the class
   clapped at the end.

2. "Tick, tock," _____ the clock.    sent    went    bent

3. Kim cut her _____ clip-ping    back    neck    hand
   the plants.

4. "Help! I am _____ fast!"         singing
   yelled Jed.             sinking    blinking

5. The flag flapped in the _____.   sand    sink    wind

6. A flock of ducks land-ed on      bank    plant    pond
   the _____.

→ Circle the correct answer.

1. Has a camel got a hump?　　**yes**　　**no**

2. Has a frog got long ears?　　**yes**　　**no**

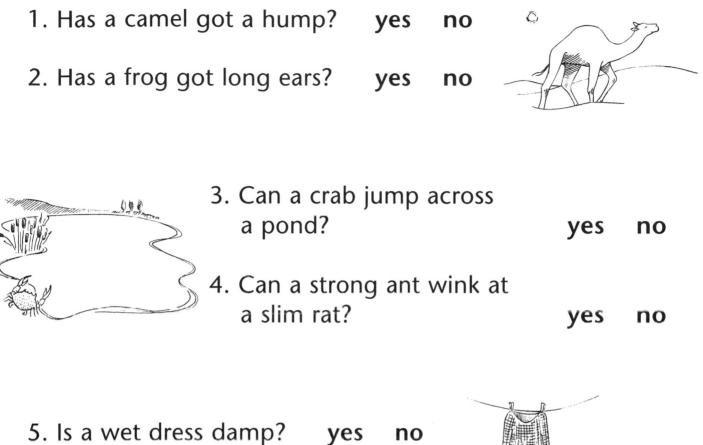

3. Can a crab jump across a pond?　　**yes**　　**no**

4. Can a strong ant wink at a slim rat?　　**yes**　　**no**

5. Is a wet dress damp?　　**yes**　　**no**

6. Will a hot dog pant?　　**yes**　　**no**

7. Can a clock run?　　**yes**　　**no**

8. Can a brass bell ring?　　**yes**　　**no**

✎ Write a story with the words. Then read the story. Check to see that it makes sense.

**felt   bump   the   his   Ling   hand   on**

_____

- - - - - - - - - - - - - - - - - - - - - - - - - -

_____

_____

- - - - - - - - - - - - - - - - - - - - - - - - - -

_____ •

✎ Write a story using the words.

**elf   sang   jump**

_____

- - - - - - - - - - - - - - - - - - - - - - - - - -

_____

_____

- - - - - - - - - - - - - - - - - - - - - - - - - -

_____

_____

- - - - - - - - - - - - - - - - - - - - - - - - - -

_____

## Lesson 12: More End Blends

| end blends | ct | ft | lt | pt | st | sk | sp |
|---|---|---|---|---|---|---|---|

Sound out the letters to read each word.

| ct | act | fact | in-sect |
|---|---|---|---|
| **ft** | gift | lift | soft |
| **lt** | melt | wilt | felt |
| **pt** | kept | swept | crept |
| **st** | last | nest | dust |
| **sk** | mask | dusk | disk |
| **sp** | clasp | gasp | lisp |

| slept | risk | belt | test |
|---|---|---|---|
| drift | left | crust | stilts |
| pact | crisp | brisk | wept |

➔ Read the words and circle the end blends. Then draw a line between the words that have the same **end** blend.

| cast | pelt | spilt | wept | midst | gasp |
|---|---|---|---|---|---|
| clasp | past | rest | tact | sift | must |
| ask | risk | sect | rust | brisk | husk |
| melt | grasp | crept | belt | lisp | tuft |

→ Write in the missing end blend. Then read the word.

**ct ft lt pt st sk sp**

de_____  sle_____  fa_____

a_____

fe_____  gi_____  cri_____

→ Choose a word from the list to complete each sentence. Write the word on the line. Then read the sentence to see that it makes sense.

**tuft   left   wilt   raft   dusk   test**

1. "Help!" yelled Deb as her _____ be-gan to sink.

2. "The spelling _____ is so long!" Jan gasped.

3. Not a muffin was _____.

4. "The plant will _____ in the sun," Mom said.

5. Glen swung his golf club and hit a _____ of grass.

6. The sun set and _____ fell.

# The Masked Bandits

 Read the story.

**The Brint Print**

**Ban-dits Rob Bank—But Cops Get Them**

At dusk, masked ban-dits held up Links Bank in Brint, rob-bing it of $20,000. They left the bank at 5:15 p.m. Then they ran to the dock, jumped onto a hid-den raft, and cast off.

As they left the land, they ran into a brisk wind. The wind up-set the raft. The ban-dits got wet. They swam back to the dock.

At 6:00 p.m. a craft be-longing to the cops picked up the ban-dits and the $20,000. The ban-dits were ar-rest-ed.

➡ Now put the sentences in the order they come in the story.

1. They left the bank at 5:15 p.m. _____

2. The cops picked up the ban-dits. _____

3. At dusk, masked ban-dits held up Links Bank. _____

4. They ran into a brisk wind. _____

✎ Write your own story using these words.

## dock   raft   wind

# Upset

Read the story.

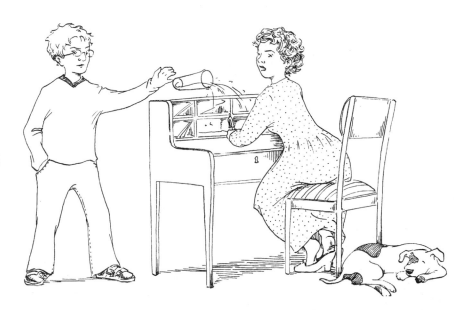

Fred felt up-set. He swept the glass off the desk, spil-ling the con-tents on Mom's best dress. Was Mom up-set! She jumped up to mop up the mess, and stepped on Spot. Was Spot up-set! He yelped and ran into Dad. Dad slipped, and was he up-set! Dad bumped into Grand-dad as he was tend-ing a plant he got as a gift. Grand-dad up-set the plant and was he up-set!

→ Now put the sentences in the order they come in the story.

Was Spot up-set!                          _____

Grand-dad up-set the plant.               _____

Dad slipped.                              _____

He swept the glass off the desk.          _____

✎ Write about what makes you upset.

_____

- - - - - - - - - - - - - - - - - - - - - - - - - - - - - - - -

_____

_____

- - - - - - - - - - - - - - - - - - - - - - - - - - - - - - - -

_____

_____

- - - - - - - - - - - - - - - - - - - - - - - - - - - - - - - -

_____

_____

- - - - - - - - - - - - - - - - - - - - - - - - - - - - - - - -

_____

✎ Write a story using these words.

**nest    crept    rest**

_____

- - - - - - - - - - - - - - - - - - - - - - - - - - - - - - - -

_____

_____

- - - - - - - - - - - - - - - - - - - - - - - - - - - - - - - -

_____

## Lesson 13: Review of Blends

| Beginning blends | bl | black |
|---|---|---|
| End blends | mp | lamp |

Read the words and circle the blends.

| glad | scrub | drift | spot |
|---|---|---|---|
| trod | sunk | crab | rung |
| plant | gift | desk | swim |

| tramp | plus | fret | dent |
|---|---|---|---|
| spring | truck | block | trip |
| clock | stilts | pink | melt |

→ Draw a line between the words that rhyme.

| hint | bent | | plum | drum |
|---|---|---|---|---|
| blank | flint | | hand | land |
| lent | Γrank | | bump | lump |

→ Write in the missing blend.

1. Carlos swe_____ up the grass clip-pings.    nt    lp    pt

2. Greta lifted the backpack and _____apped it on her back.    spl    str    scr

3. The raft drift-ed from the land and sa_____.    sk    nk    ct

4. The in-sect was _____apped in the web.    tr    st    nt

5. The Hunts rent-ed a te_____ and went camp-ing.    mp    nd    nt

6. Cliff jumped into bed, pulled up the soft blan-kets, and sle_____.    sp    pl    pt

7. Dad tripped and fell _____at on his back.    lt    pl    fl

8. Stella flung the brick into the po_____.    nt    nd    lt

→ Circle the name of the picture.

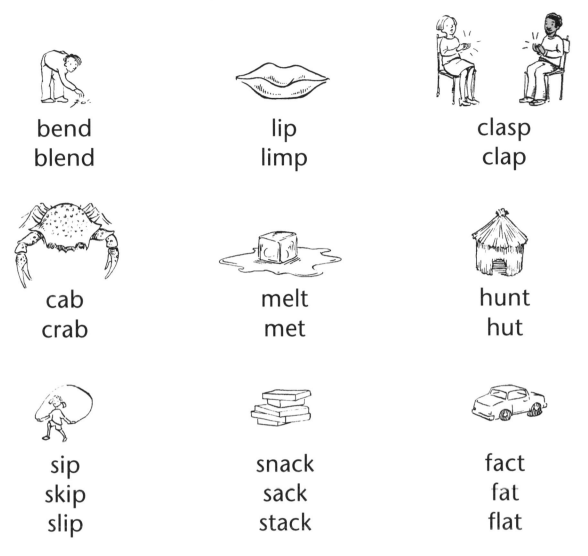

bend
blend

lip
limp

clasp
clap

cab
crab

melt
met

hunt
hut

sip
skip
slip

snack
sack
stack

fact
fat
flat

→ Draw a line to the correct ending of each sentence.

1. Jack filled the mug

2. Nesim helped him-self

3. Pat cracked six eggs

into the pan.

to the brim.

to a hot dog and bun.

4. Don skipped class

5. Tanya did well

6. Bud was last

to hang up his jack-et.

and went swim-ming.

on the spell-ing test.

# Bren-da and Brad's Camp-ing Trip

Read the story. Below each picture, write the number of the paragraph that tells about it.

Learn to read these words:   **there**   **their**

**1.** Bren-da and Brad were off on a camp-ing trip. They helped their Mom and Dad pack a tent, blan-kets, mat-tress-es, a grill, a pic-nic bas-ket, and **their** back-packs into their van.

**2.** They left at 7:00 a.m. and got **there** at 2 p.m. They put on **their** sun block. They un-packed the van.

_____

_____

**3.** Then Bren-da and Dad dragged the tent to the bank of a pond. **There** they hit sticks into the grass. Then Dad held up the tent as Brenda fas-tened the tent strings to the sticks.

**4.** As Bren-da and Dad put up the tent, Brad helped Mom set up the grill. Then he got the pic-nic bas-ket and un-packed hot dogs, buns, and a bag of plums. Mom got a sal-ad she had put into a plas-tic bag to stop it from wilt-ing.

_____

**5.** Next, Bren-da and Dad went swim-ming in the pond as Brad and Mom grilled the hot dogs and fixed the sal-ad.

_____

**6.** They had **their** pic-nic at dusk.

**7.** Then they crept into **their** tent, pulled the flap a-cross, and slept.

_____

_____

_____

✎ Write about 3 things that Brad and Dad did.

✎ Write a story about the picture. Use at least 3 of these words in your story.

**truck**   **bumped**
   **skidded**
**flat**   **spilt**   **milk**

_____

_____

_____

_____

_____

_____

_____

_____

_____

# The Swinging Animal Rock Quintet

Read the story. See if you can you tell
what **quin-tet** means. Is it 2, 5, or 7?

A frog jumped up on-to a rock
on the bank of the pond. She had her snack of wil-ted
plants. Then she sat in the sun and sang a song:

She wept as she swept,
And gasped as she grasped.
She slept as she crept,
And smelt as she felt.
Sing a song
Sing a-long!

She bumped as she jumped,
And blinked as she winked,
She bent as she went,
And swung as she sung.
Sing a song
Sing a-long!

As she sang the last "sing a-long," a rob-in land-ed
next to her on the rock.

"Sing a-long, sing the song," the frog said to the
rob-in.

"I can't sing non-sense songs," the rob-in said.

"But rock songs are of-ten non-sense," said the frog.
She pat-ted the rock she was sit-ting on and grinned. "Get
it? It's a **rock** song!"

"Yes, I get it, but I
still can't sing it," said
the rob-in. Then she
add-ed, "But I will
peck on the rock as
you sing."

"OK," said the frog, and she be-gan to sing.

Just then an in-sect crept from its nest.

"Sing a-long, sing the song," said the frog to the in-sect.

"I can't sing, but I can hum," said the in-sect, and he flapped his wings and hummed.

"OK," said the frog, and the in-sect jumped onto the rock.

They be-gan the song, but as they did a crick-et hopped up.

"Sing a-long, sing the song," said the frog.

"I can't sing, but I can click, click, click just as cas-tin-ets," said the crick-et. He rubbed his wings and there was a click, click, click-ing.

"Swell!" said the frog, "hop on!"

The crick-et hopped on-to the rock and the an-i-mals be-gan the song.

Just then a pos-sum trot-ted up.

"Sing a-long, sing the song," said the frog.

"I can't sing well, I've got a lisp," said the pos-sum. Then he added, "But I can con-duct you!" He held up his stick and jumped on-to the rock.

And so be-gan the Swing-ing An-i-mal Rock Quin-tet!

→ Circle the correct answer.

A quin-tet = (a) 2 (b) 5 (c) 7

✎ Choose one of the an-i-mals in the Swinging An-i-mal Rock Quin-tet and write about what he or she did.

**robin   frog   insect   cricket   pos-sum**

✎ Write a song of 4 lines for the rock quintet to sing. See if you can make the words rhyme at the ends of the lines.

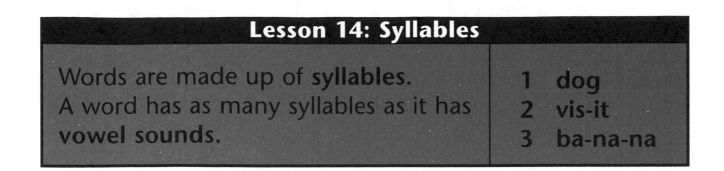

# Lesson 14: Syllables

Words are made up of **syllables**.
A word has as many syllables as it has **vowel sounds**.

1  dog
2  vis-it
3  ba-na-na

Say the name of the picture. Then circle the number of vowel sounds it has.

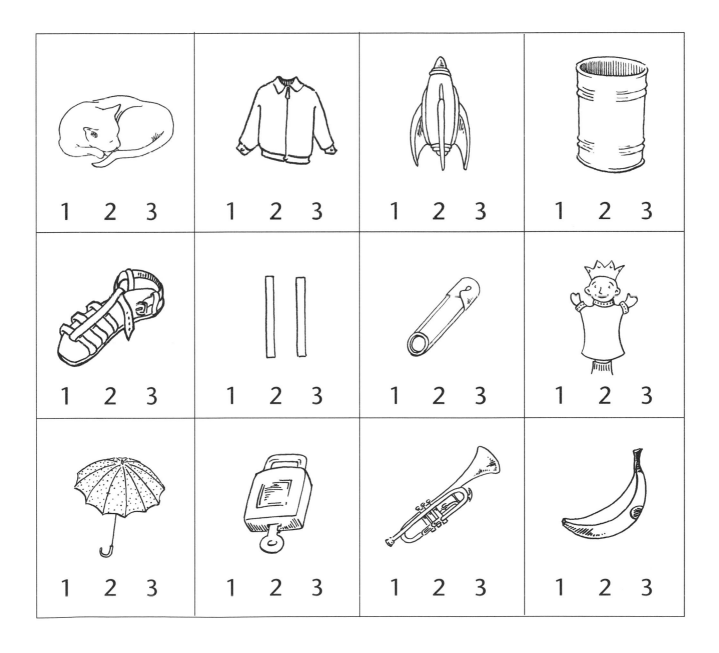

| 1  2  3 | 1  2  3 | 1  2  3 | 1  2  3 |
| 1  2  3 | 1  2  3 | 1  2  3 | 1  2  3 |
| 1  2  3 | 1  2  3 | 1  2  3 | 1  2  3 |

→ Circle the vowel sounds. Then write the number of syllables in the word.

p(i)cn(i)c    __2__        puppet    _____        desk      _____

unpack    _____          bump      _____        lemon     _____

luck      _____          hit       _____        fled      _____

swimming  _____          crisp     _____        pumpkin   _____

packet    _____          bottom    _____        beginning _____

insect    _____          clock     _____        fabric    _____


→ Draw a line between the beginning and end of each word.

| rab | bit | kit | ten | blan | ton |
| mit | et | bas | ket | lem | ket |
| jack | ten | sev | en | but | on |

| sing | set | clos | et | Grand | pet |
| hid | den | muf | fin | pup | kin |
| up | ing | un | pack | pump | dad |

→ Put an X in the box next to the sentence that tells about the picture.

☐ The man pulled a rabbit from his jacket pocket.

☐ The man undid the buttons of his jacket.

☐ Mom put the lemons into a plastic bag.

☐ Dad got a packet from the cabinet.

☐ Pamela was upset. She got a traffic ticket.

☐ Anton lost his umbrella and got wet.

☐ There was a big plop as the rock sank to the bottom of the pond.

☐ There was a sudden bang as the rocket went off.

# At the Rapids

Read the story about an animal. What do you think it is—a rabbit, a camel, or a cub?

Learn to read this word: **by**

Learn to read these words and find their meanings:
**rapids**　**salmon**

An animal suns himself on the banks of the rapids in Alaska. Then, quick as a wink, he jumps in. He hits the bottom fast and traps a pink salmon. He grasps the salmon in his lips, pulls himself back onto the bank, and has his snack.

The animal's twin and his dad stand in the rapids. His twin gets a salmon by stamping on it. His dad gets a salmon by batting it onto the bank.

It is not difficult to get the salmon. It is the end of spring and the salmon are swimming up the rapids to drop their eggs.

→ Circle the correct answer.

1. The animal is  (a) a rabbit  (b) a camel  (c) a cub

2. The animal is from  (a) Montana  (b) Alaska
                                (c) Wisconsin

3. The animals are getting  (a) crabs  (b) clams  (c) salmon

✎ Write about how the cub gets his snack.

The well-fed animal is an Alaskan cub. Adults get as big and strong as 18 men! But they can still run at a quick trot.

Adults nap in a den in the hills until spring. Then they snack on grasses, animals, and plants until the salmon swim up the rapids.

→ Circle the correct answer.

1. The adults get as big and strong as  (a) 8  (b) 18  (c) 80 men

2. The adult's den is  (a) on the bank of the rapids
                              (b) on the grasslands  (c) in the hills

3. The adults do not snack on  (a) plants  (b) bananas
                                      (c) grasses

✎ Write a story about a cub who wakes up on the first day of spring. Tell some of the things he or she might do.

# Benjamin Franklin

📘 Read the story.

Learn to read these words: **great  son  school  when**

Benjamin Franklin was a **great** man. He was **wise** and helpful. He had fun **inventing** things. He lived from 1706 until 1790.

Ben lived in Boston. He was the tenth and last **son**. In fact, he was the tenth and last **son** of a last son, of a last **son**, of a last **son**, of a last **son**—back to his great-great granddad.

The Franklin kids had jobs. Sam was a blacksmith. Jim did printing. 3 kids helped their dad fixing candles (can-duls). But Ben went to **school** when he was seven.

→ Circle the correct answer.

1. Benjamin Franklin was  (a) sad  (b) sick  (c) wise

2. Ben lived  (a) from 1760–1790  (b) from 1706–1790
            (c) from 1607–1790

3. Ben lived in  (a) Boston  (b) Hampton  (c) Dedham

4. Jim's job was  (a) a blacksmith  (b) in printing
              (c) fixing candles

5. Ben  (a) fixed candles  (b) went to school
        (c) helped Sam

**When** Ben was ten, he left **school**. He ran **errands**, dipped candles, and went swimming. He had fun. **When** he was 12, his dad said he must get a job.

Ben said he was not into fixing candles. It smelled! The hot wax had a **disgusting** smell. He said a job as a blacksmith was too hot. They visited a lot of jobs, but Ben said, "No, no, no" to the jobs. In the end, he went into printing, helping Jim.

Jim was **strict** and stopped Ben from having fun. Ben read (red) a lot. He was thinking of things to invent.

**When** Ben was 17, he ran off to Philadelphia (Fil-a-del-fi-a).

→ Circle the correct answer.

1. Ben left school when he was  (a) 7  (b) 10  (c) 12

2. The candles were not   (a) red   (b) full of hot wax
                           (c) strong smelling

3. Ben got a job  (a) in printing  (b) at a blacksmith's
                           (c) fixing candles

4. When he was at Jim's, Ben  (a) had a lot of fun
      (b) was thinking of things to invent
      (c) invented the printing press

5. Ben ran off to  (a) Boston  (b) Philadelphia
                           (c) back to his dad

Ben Franklin was glad to be in Philadelphia. He met Debbie (Deb-bee) there and they were wed. He went into printing and did well. He and Debbie were selling things, too: wax, maps, cod, cloth, and Mr. Franklin's candles. The selling went well, too.

In 1732, Franklin printed an almanac. An almanac is full of odd facts. It tells **when** the sun will set, **when** it will be hot, and **when** to plant. The almanac was funny and it was a **great** hit.

Benjamin Franklin **seldom** rested. He was a fun and **talented** man. He lived until he was 84.

➜ Circle the correct answer.

1. Ben Franklin was  (a) mad  (b) sad  (c) glad to be in Philadelphia.

2. The Franklins were selling  (a) maps (b) cups  (c) jackets

3. An almanac has  (a) maps  (b) stories
                              (c) lots of odd facts

4. Ben lived until he was  (a) 64  (b) 74  (c) 84

➜ Now reread the story and then circle the correct answer.

The story happens  (a) in the present  (b) in the past

➜ Find these words in the story:  **errand   seldom   talented**

Then match the words with their meanings.

_____ 1. errand    (a) skillful, gifted

_____ 2. seldom    (b) a trip, often helpful, to get things

_____ 3. talented  (c) not often

➔ Put the sentences in the order they come in the story.

____ Jim was **strict** and stopped Ben from having fun.

____ He was the tenth and last **son**.

____ Ben Franklin was a **talented** man.

____ He went into printing and did well.

✎ Write a story using one of these words.

**wise    disgusting    invented    strict**

You have read a story about Benjamin Franklin's life. Now tell about your life. You can write about when you were born, how old you are, where you live, what you like to do, who your best friend is, or what you would wish for if you could have a wish.

**Part Two**

Long Vowels
and Syllables

# Lesson 16: Long Vowels

The **vowels** are **a e i o u** and sometimes y and **w**.
Vowels are **long** when they **say their name**.

Say the name of the picture. Then circle the one with the
long vowel sound.

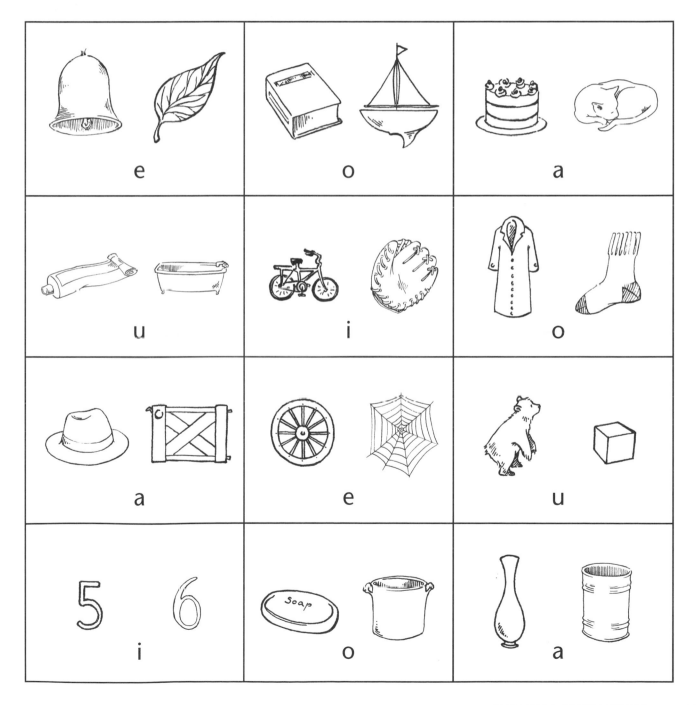

e          o          a

u          i          o

a          e          u

i          o          a

→ Say the name of the picture and circle the long vowel you hear.

o a u

i e o

a i o

a e u

o u i

u o e

e i o

a u e

i u a

a o u

i e o

u i o

➔ Put a slash mark through the words that have the short vowel sound. The word that is left on each line has the long vowel sound.

Remember the rule for short vowels: Vowels are short when there is one vowel followed by only consonants.

| a | lamp | Dad | cake | wag | ran |
|---|------|-----|------|-----|-----|
| e | bed | end | wet | tree | mess |
| i | did | mix | lip | kite | fill |
| o | box | boat | jog | top | lock |
| u | bus | rub | cute | hum | tug |

➔ Look at the pictures. Then add a vowel to each word to name the picture. All the words are long vowel words.

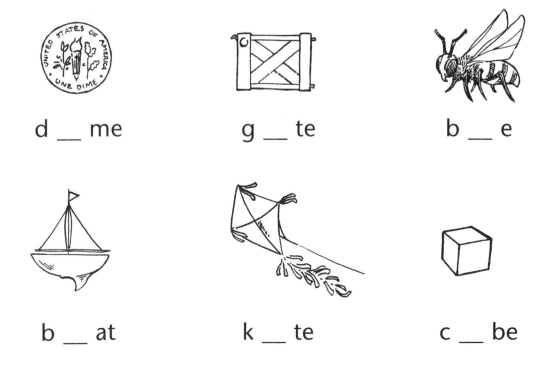

d __ me          g __ te          b __ e

b __ at          k __ te          c __ be

✎ Write the words in the correct order to find out what Jake is doing. Is Jake a long or a short vowel word?

1. and   bat   swung   his   missed

Jake _____

_____ .

2. mitten   his   lost   off   cap   his   and   fell

Jake _____

and _____ .

3. tripped   ran   and   fell   and   fast

Jake _____

_____ .

4. bat   his   left   went   and   swimming

Jake _____

_____ .

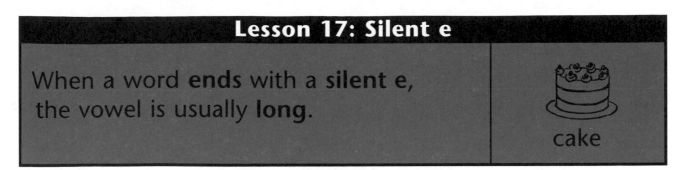

# Lesson 17: Silent e

When a word **ends** with a **silent e**, the vowel is usually **long**.

cake

Sound out the letters to read each word.

| a | bake | gate | made | same | tale | wave |
|---|------|------|------|------|------|------|
|   | plane | ate | sale | late | grape | game |

| i | hide | mine | mile | dime | bike | five |
|---|------|------|------|------|------|------|
|   | pine | kite | like | life | fine | side |

| o | hope | robe | woke | stove | note | stole |
|---|------|------|------|-------|------|-------|
|   | joke | rode | vote | slope | hole | globe |

| u | cube | cute | rule | use | tune | rude |
|---|------|------|------|-----|------|------|
|   | mule | prune | tube | fumes | flute | dude |

| e | Pete | Eve | Steve | compete | complete |
|---|------|-----|-------|---------|----------|

→ Draw a line between the words that rhyme.

| mad      made | hid       hide | hope       hop | cube      cub |
|---|---|---|---|
| fade      bad | side       lid | top       slope | rub      tube |
| line      mine | lock      stole | bake      take | Eve      tell |
| win      fin | pole      sock | lap      tap | bell      Steve |

→ Circle the name of the picture.

| | | |
|---|---|---|
| like    bike<br><br>line    side | globe    rode<br><br>robe    note | flute    use<br><br>June    tune |
| gate    wave<br><br>sale    grapes | bone    brute<br><br>bake    bike | take    twine<br><br>pile    pole |
| same    time<br><br>home    tune | drove    drive<br><br>dive    Dave | plane    pine<br><br>pane    poke |
| strike    stake<br><br>Steve    stove | prune    trade<br><br>rode    pride | dome    male<br><br>dime    mule |

➜ Add a silent **e** to find the name of each picture. Then write the number of the picture in the box.

☐ hik___    ☐ wav__    ☐ tub___    ☐ ston__

☐ scal__    ☐ pil___    ☐ glob__    ☐ can___

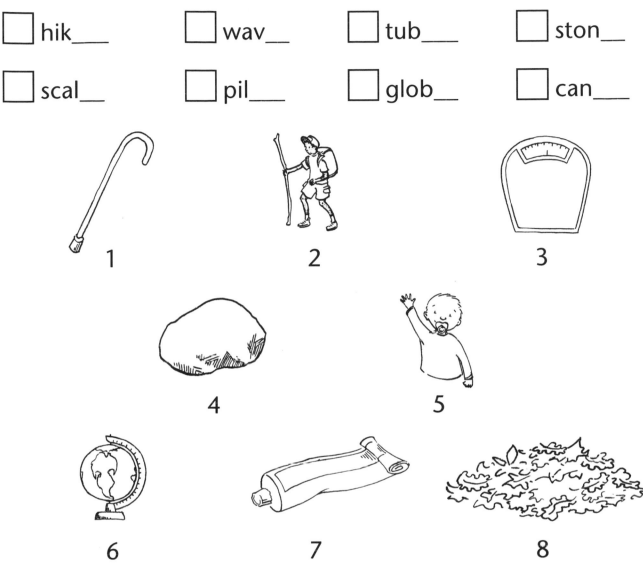

1

2

3

4

5

6

7

8

➜ Change the vowel to make a new word.

| pole | p___le | drove | dr___ve | grope | gr___pe |
|------|--------|-------|---------|-------|---------|
| Luke | l___ke | brake | br___ke | cone | c___ne |
| pane | p___ne | role | r___le | mule | m___le |
| wide | w___de | tame | t___me | daze | d___ze |

→ Circle the silent **e** words.

| plan | kit | bus |
|---|---|---|
| plane | kitten | us |
| plant | kite | use |

| bank | pink |
|---|---|
| bake | pin |
| back | pine |

| rod | like | slope |
|---|---|---|
| rode | lick | slip |
| rotten | luck | slap |

→ Write in the missing letters. Then read the sentence to see that it makes sense.

1. Nicole's bike has a flat ___ire.            f     t     l

2. Pete broke a ___one in his hand.       d     b     p

3. Steve smiled as he was given the ____ize.    p     pl     pr

4. Kate's red robe will ___ade in the sun.    f     m     w

5. "Can Jane and I skate on the ___ake?"    b     t     l

6. Rose closed the gate and ___aved to Dave.   s     c     w

➡ Read the sentence and circle the missing word.

1. Dale hid Mike's bike as a
   (a) broke  (b) spoke  (c) joke

2. It used to cost a __ to ride the bus.
   (a) dine  (b) dime  (c) time

3. "I am __ today," said Abe.  (a) line  (b) nine  (c) mine

4. Eve ate the last bite of the date-nut cake Mom
   (a) made  (b) fade  (c) wade

5. Ted will prune his prize __ in June.
   (a) noses  (b) poses  (c) roses

6. They left the __ at five and got home at seven.
   (a) same  (b) game  (c) gale

7. Luke put the cubes of ham into the pan on the
   (a) stove  (b) strove  (c) stole

8. "I __ you will not be late," said Mr. Dodd.
   (a) vote  (b) note  (c) hope

→ Put an X in the box next to the sentence that tells about the picture.

☐ Jane had a date and she was late.

☐ Jade ate a date and put the stone on a plate.

☐ "It's a strike! Justin can save the game!" yelled Dale.

☐ "Mom! Mom! I can swim nine strokes!" yelled Jake.

☐ Luke rode a mule into the Grand Canyon.

☐ Rose jumped on her bike, waved to Mom, and rode along the lane.

☐ "Excuse me, can you tell me the time?" asked Eve.

☐ "Steve slid into second base," yelled Rafe.

→ Put an X on the line next to the statements that are correct.

1. A cube has six sides. _____

2. A tune can be sung. _____

3. A cake can be made. _____

4. Smoke does not come from fire. _____

5. Roses can be put in a vase. _____

6. A clock cannot strike. _____

7. You get grapes from a vine. _____

8. A stove will not get hot. _____

9. You can ride a mule. _____

10. You cannot glide on skates. _____

→ Match the words with their meanings.

____ 1. hate  (a) smile       ____ 1. rock  (a) stone

____ 2. same  (b) dislike     ____ 2. tale  (b) to make fun

____ 3. grin  (c) alike       ____ 3. joke  (c) story

# Letter to Mike

Read the letter that Dad left for Mike.

Learn to read this word: **dear**

Dear Mike,

Just a quick note to tell you I will be home late. I will not have time to fix the ham and eggplant. Will you:

1:
- Take the ham off the bone and cut it into cubes.
- Scrape and cut up the carrots.
- Put the ham and carrots into the pan.
- Put the pan in the stove to bake at 350°.

2:
- Wipe the eggplant and divide it into nine strips.
- Dip the strips in the crumbs.
- Put the strips into a pan of hot, melted fat.
- Bake the strips until they are crisp.

You are a big help!

Dad

P.S. Hope you had a great time at the game.

→ Reread the letter slowly and carefully so you can remember the details and answer the questions. Then circle the correct answer.

1. Mike did <u>not</u> have to cut up
   (a) a ham  (b) a yam  (c) an eggplant

2. Mike had to scrape
   (a) the carrots  (b) the crusts  (c) the eggplant

3. Mike had to put _____ into the pan.
   (a) the ham  (b) the carrots  (c) the ham and carrots

4. Mike had to put the eggplant strips
   (a) in the crumbs and then the fat
   (b) in the fat and then the crumbs

5. Mike had to bake the eggplant until it was
   (a) limp  (b) crisp  (c) hot

6. Mike came home from
   (a) school  (b) a game  (c) a pal's home

✎ Now reread the letter to see if you can find the 17 **silent e** words. Circle them. Count each **silent e** word even if it is repeated.

✎ Dad gave Mike directions to fix the ham and eggplant. Write the directions to make a dish you like. List the items you need. Then write the steps you must take to make it.

# Off to Camp

Read the story.

Learn the meaning of this word:  **quotes** = " "

Quotes are used to show that people are talking. In this story Jane and Eve are talking.

"I suppose you will be off to camp in June. Do you like it?" asked Jane.

"Yes, it's fun," said Eve. "We hike. We swim and dive in the lake. We ride bikes. We compete in a lot of games. And at the end, we have a festival, a parade, and prizes. Last time we had a kite festival. We made kites from sticks, bits of twine, and odds and ends. The best kites got prizes."

"Did you get a prize?" asked Jane.

"No. Mine fell to bits just as I got it up!" said Eve.

"It's a long trip to get to camp, isn't it? I suppose you have to ride the bus alone?"

"Yes, but I like it," said Eve.

"Aren't you homesick being miles from home?" asked Jane.

"No. Well, not often. I have lots of pals there. And we kid and joke a lot," said Eve. Then she gave a smile and added, "We make up cute jokes." "Tell me a joke," said Jane. "OK," said Eve:

Sam: "Dr., Dr. I've got just 59 seconds to live!"
Dr.: "I'll be with you in a minute."

Jane grinned at the joke. "Yes, that is a cute joke," she said. "It must be fun at camp. I bet you will be glad to get there."

"Yes," said Eve. "I hope it's as great as last time."

→ Number the sentences in the order they come in the story.

"Aren't you homesick being miles from home?"        _____

"I suppose you will be off to camp in June."        _____

"I hope it's as great as last time."        _____

"It's a long trip to get to camp, isn't it?"        _____

✎ Pretend you went to a camp. Write a note to a pal telling the things you did there.

# A Twin Tale

Read the story and see if you can tell the lesson.

Learn to read these words that have a long vowel sound:

**kind  find  behind  blind  mind  rind  bind  wind**

Jake and Jack were twins, but they were not alike. Jake was full of himself and rude. Jack was wise and **kind**.

They lived at home until they were adults. Then they set off to find wives. The tale tells of their trip.

Jake strode along. He left Jack **behind**, but Jack did not **mind**. He just hummed a tune. He admired the plants and spoke to animals. He met up with Jake at a mole hill.

"Let's kick the mole's hill and wake him up," grinned Jake.

"No, you must not kick the mole hill. It is his home," said Jack.

Jake smiled and said, "It's just a joke."

"It's not a joke, it's his home. You must not kick it," said Jack.

They went on and came to a lake.

A duck was swimming on the lake. Jake said, "Let's grab the duck, make a fire, and have a snack."

"Let the duck alone," said Jack. "You must not take the life of an animal."

They went on until they came to a hill.

There a snake was resting in the sun beside a hole. The hole held a nest and five eggs.

"Snakes alive!" joked Jake. Then he added, "Let's hide the eggs and put stones in the nest."

"No, let her eggs alone. You must not take the eggs," said Jack.

At last they came to a fine, big home.

"It must be the home of a king," guessed Jake. "I bet we will find a wife there."

Jack and Jack went in, but no one was there . . . well, no one alive! The men and women inside the home were made of stone.

"I bet there is a spell on the home," said Jake.

"Yes," said Jack. Then he spotted a note. It said: "To unlock the spell of stone and win the hands of June and Jan, the king's twins, you must find 2 rings. Take the spade and dig in the grass by the lake. There you will **find** the rings."

"Fine!" said Jake. "I will **find** the ring. I am strong and fast. It will not take me long!" He grabbed the spade and strode off.

Jack was left behind, as he often was. But he did not care. He just hummed a tune and dozed off.

At last, Jake came back. But he had no rings. He was mad. He went back to check the note, but when he picked it up, he fell into the spell and became stone, too—a mad Jake made of stone!

"Oh, no!" said Jack. "I must **find** the rings and save Jake."

Like Jake, Jack used the spade to dig. But he did not find the rings. He was just giving up as the mole came along.

"You saved my home. I will help you," the mole said. He began to dig in the grass. Time went by. At last, Jack spotted a red box in the hole. Inside was a note.

The note said: "You must **find** a black box at the bottom of the lake."

"Oh, no!" said Jack. "I can't hope to **find** the box. I can't swim. I can't dive to the bottom of the lake!"

As Jack ran to the lake, the duck swam up.

"You saved me. I will help you," he said. "I will **find** the box." And he did.

Inside the box was—you guessed it—no rings, but a note. The note said: "You will **find** the rings in a cave. The cave is in the rocks by the lake."

Jack went to the rocks, but the cave was blocked by a big stone.

"Oh, no!" said Jack. "I can't get in. I must get the rings to save Jake."

"No problem," said the snake as she slid up. "You saved my eggs. I will help you. I can slide in. I can get the rings."

She slid into the crack in the rocks and came back grasping the rings.

The snake gave the rings to Jack. Jack ran to the home. There was Jake, wide awake. Jack had broken the spell!

And there were the twins, June and Jan, the king, and the men and women. They were not stone. They were full of smiles.

"You have saved us!" said the king. "You and Jake can wed my twins. In time, you, Jack, will become king. You broke the spell."

Jake and Jack put the rings on June and Jan's hands. The twins hugged the twins. The men and women clapped.

Jake slapped Jack on the back and said, "I am grateful to you. You are my best pal. I will try to be like you."

➔   The lesson of the story is: If you are _____ you will be given _____ness back.

✎ Write your own story about twins.

## Lesson 18: Regular Double Vowels ai and ay

When two vowels come together, the **first** one is **long** and the **second** one is **silent**.

| | |
|---|---|
| rain | tray |

Sound out the letters to read each word.

| | | | |
|---|---|---|---|
| pain | say | wait | fail |
| way | laid | day | main |
| mail | lay | aim | tail |
| ray | train | pail | pay |

| | | | |
|---|---|---|---|
| play | snail | stain | braids |
| rain | grain | brain | gray |
| explain | today | crayon | Sunday |
| exclaim | waist | complain | detail |

Learn to read this word:   **always**

➔ Draw a line between the words that rhyme.

| | | | | | |
|---|---|---|---|---|---|
| stay | maid | train | sail | nail | sway |
| rain | tray | stray | Spain | paid | frail |
| paid | drain | wail | pray | spray | raid |

→ Circle the name of the picture.

| | | | |
|---|---|---|---|
| paid<br>pain<br>paint<br>plain | nail<br>mail<br>maid<br>may | stain<br>strain<br>drain<br>train | stay<br>spray<br>say<br>ray |

| | | | |
|---|---|---|---|
| raid<br>trade<br>grades<br>braids | sail<br>stale<br>snail<br>snake | gate<br>date<br>wait<br>bait | compete<br>complete<br>contain<br>complain |

→ Write in the missing letters. Then read the sentence to see that it makes sense.

1. The Uptons ____ways visit their granddad on Sundays.

ex    re    al

2. The snail left a ____ail as it went on its way.

dr    tr    br

3. "Are you ____aying long?" asked Vic.

sm    sl    st

4. "Don't ____omplain, you will not have to wait long," said Joe.

r    w    c

5. The box contained twelve ____ayons.

br    tr    cr

6. "The ____ain is blocked again!" exclaimed Gabe in despair.

gr    dr    br

7. Ms. Gait's class always puts on a play in ____ay.

p    d    M

8. "I have to ____ay the bills and mail the letters by next week," Mom said.

s    p    r

➔ Write in the correct word. Then put an X in the box next to the sentence that tells about the picture.

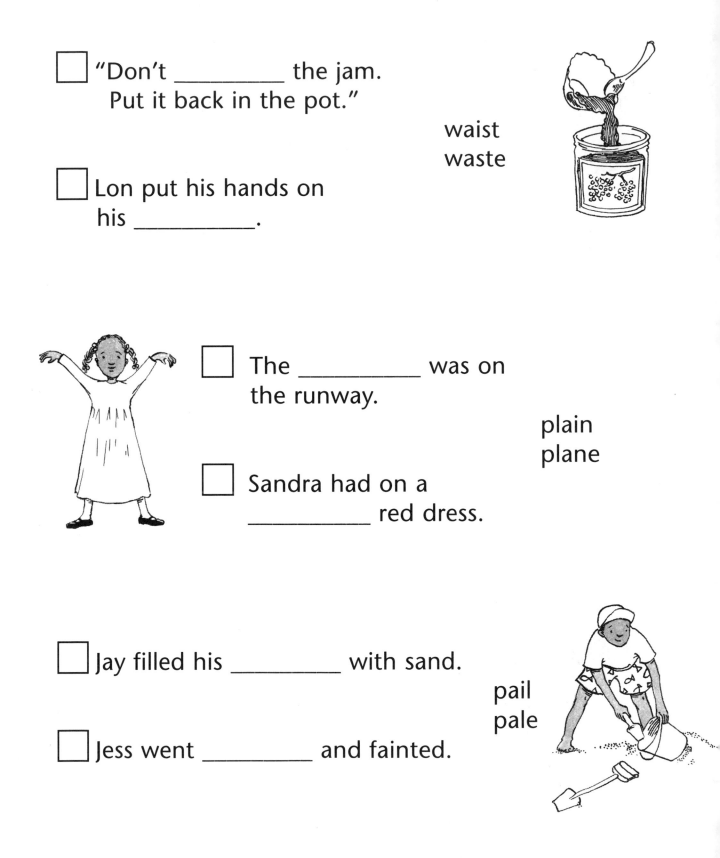

☐ "Don't _____ the jam. Put it back in the pot."

☐ Lon put his hands on his _____ .

waist
waste

☐ The _____ was on the runway.

☐ Sandra had on a _____ red dress.

plain
plane

☐ Jay filled his _____ with sand.

☐ Jess went _____ and fainted.

pail
pale

# Louis Braille

Read the story slowly to remember the details. Find the word **combined** and see if you can figure out its meaning.

"I am blind. I cannot tell of men and happenings. But I will find a way to," said Louis Braille in 1822. He was 13 then. By the time he was 15 he had invented a way.

Braille developed a way to read by using his finger-tips. He made up a code of six raised dots. He **combined** the dots in 63 ways. Then he "read" by running his fingertips across the dots.

Today the blind still use Braille's way to read.

➜ Circle the correct answer.

1. Combined =  (a) raised  (b) mixed  (c) ran

2. Braille invented his way to read in  (a) 1824  (b) 1863

3. Braille was then  (a) 13  (b) 15

4. Braille read by  (a) putting on glasses
    (b) using his fingertips

5. Braille's code was made up of  (a) raised dots
    (b) raised lines

6. The system the blind use to read is
    named _____.

7. Match the words with their meanings.

    _____  1. to invent  (a) to make up, to develop
    _____  2. to raise     (b) to lift up

✎ Write about 3 things you would miss if you were blind.

## Lesson 19: Regular Double Vowels ee

When two vowels come together, the **first** one is **long** and the **second** one is **silent**.

tree

Sound out the letters to read each word.

| | | | |
|---|---|---|---|
| see | feet | feel | seem |
| deep | week | need | bee |
| feed | peel | keep | beef |
| eel | free | seed | heel |

| | | | |
|---|---|---|---|
| sleep | flee | deer | weed |
| coffee | green | breeze | sweep |
| speed | sleeve | queen | agree |
| between | bleed | fifteen | nineteen |

→ Use a word from the lists above to answer each riddle.

1. You stand on _____.

2. Seven days = a _____.

3. It buzzes—a _____.

4. Glasses help you to _____.

5. A cut will _____.

6. You get into bed to _____.

7. You can find it on a dress and a jacket. It's a _____.

8. Six and nine = _____.

9. You can drink it— _____.

10. It's a wind—a _____.

→ Add **ee** to find the name of the picture. Then write the number of the picture in the box.

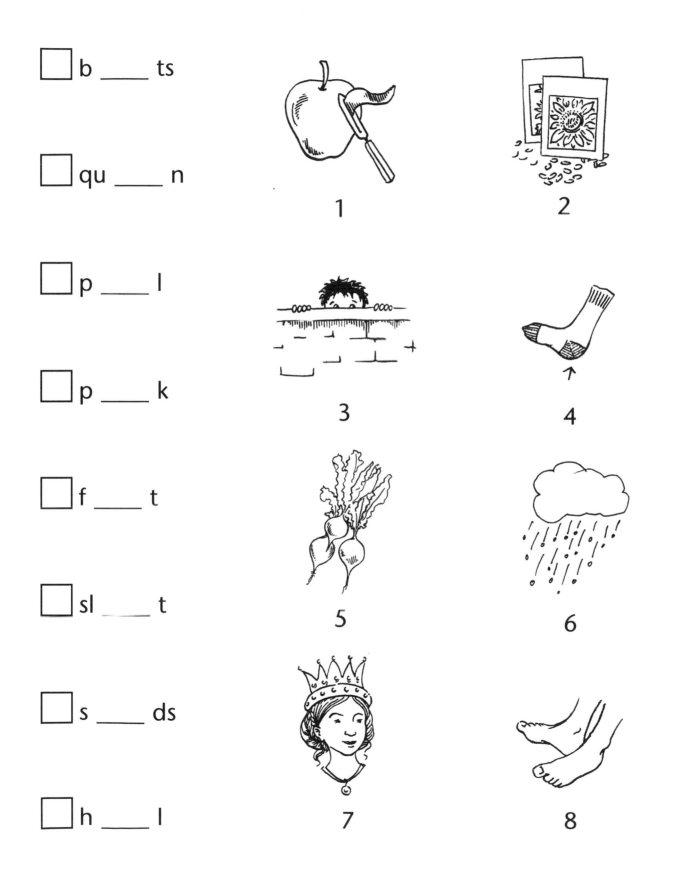

☐ b ____ ts

☐ qu ____ n

1

2

☐ p ____ l

☐ p ____ k

3

4

☐ f ____ t

☐ sl ____ t

5

6

☐ s ____ ds

☐ h ____ l

7

8

→ Read the sentence and circle the missing word.

1. You will get a traffic ticket if you  (a) weed  (b) need
    (c) speed

2. The cut will stop __ if you put a Band-Aid on it.
    (a) speeding  (b) bleeding  (c) feeding

3. Last weekend Nadeem and Jen came to see me in their
    (a) deep  (b) jeep  (c) tree

4. If you are not feeling well you can __ late.  (a) steep
    (b) creep  (c) sleep

5. It __ as if I've spent the entire day pulling up weeds!
    (a) seems  (b) seen  (c) sweet

6. "Next __ we will have a spelling test," said Mr. Peel.
    (a) weed  (b) week  (c) weep

7. A soft __ made the trees sway.  (a) squeeze  (b) sneeze
    (c) breeze

8. "Will you __ up the packet of seeds I have spilled?"
    asked Lee.  (a) steep  (b) sleep  (c) sweep

➔ Put an X next to the sentence that tells about the picture.

☐ Brad peeled and cut up the beets.

☐ Ken squeezed the lemons.

☐ Emma sneezed nineteen times.

☐ The bee stung Greta on the neck.

☐ The deer kicked up its heels.

☐ The eel slid between the rocks.

➔ Circle the word that does <u>not</u> fit in each sentence.

1. Ron closed the screen to stop the jet from coming in.

2. Sandra feeds her pet melon 2 times a day.

3. Mom put the beef in the sun to freeze it.

4. Dad drove his deer up the street.

5. Dave put on his socks as he feet were wet.

6. Jill sweetened the coffee by putting a stone into the cup.

7. There are 7 seconds in a week.

8. Lee put the beets into the big pan as it was full.

# Mr. Green's Grapes

This story is for you to practice reading **ee** words. See if you can find all 61 of them! Circle them. Count each **ee** word even if it is repeated.

Learn to read these words:  **them  ever never  one  done**

Mr. Green had been tending his vine a long time. He had weeded it. He had trained it along a trellis. And he had made a screen to keep off the breezes. But it still had no grapes.

Weeks passed. Then, at last, Mr. Green spotted not **one**, but fifteen, wee grapes!

"Yes," he said to himself with glee as he got up close and peered at **them**. "Yes, there are indeed fifteen grapes."

He went on tending the vine until the grapes became plump and green. Then he gave **one** a squeeze and said to himself, "Yes, they are indeed ripe. It is time to pick **them**."

He picked the grapes and put **them** on a plate in the sun.

"They are the best grapes I have **ever** seen. And I bet they are sweet as well," he said. "I can't wait to have **them**. But I will keep **them** until I have **done** the jobs I must do. Let's see, I must feed Fee-Fee his greens, fix the beef, peel the beets, and then dust and sweep up."

He fed his pet rabbit, Fee-Fee, and did his jobs. Then he said, "Well, I've **done** the jobs, but I'll keep the grapes until I've had a nap."

He went to see that the grapes were still there, and then he lay on the grass and went to sleep.

As he slept, Sid, a kid living up the street from Mr. Green, peeked in the half-closed gate. He spotted the ripe, green grapes. And he spotted Mr. Green fast asleep.

He ran in, picked up the grapes, stuffed **them** in his jacket, and left!

Mr. Green woke up. "Oh, no," he wailed, "Sid has taken the grapes. I'll **never** get to eat **them**!"

He was mad. He had been longing to have the grapes.

"I didn't spend weeks tending the vine to feed Sid!" he said. And then he added, "He needs a lesson! He must not take things that are not his."

He racked his brains. "I've got it!" he said. He went up the street, seeking Sid.

He spotted him sitting by the creek, wiping his lips on the back of his sleeve.

"Hi!" Mr. Green said, greeting Sid. "I see you have been having a snack."

Sid gave him a wide smile and said, "Hi, Mr. Green."

Mr. Green said to Sid, "Are you feeling OK? You seem to be a bit pale."

"Yes, I feel fine," said Sid.

"You do not seem well to me," said Mr. Green. "I seem to have lost the ripe grapes. Have you seen **them**?"

"No, I haven't seen **them**," said Sid.

"Oh, dear, I hope no one stole **them**. The grapes can make you sick," said Mr. Green.

"Sick?" asked Sid.

"Yes, the seeds inside can make you quite sick."

"Oh, no! Oh, no!" exclaimed Sid, jumping up.

"There, I said you did not seem well," said Mr. Green. "You had best run along home." He gave Sid a big smile and left.

Sid crept home and waited.

➔ Did you find the **ee** words? Now reread the story and decide on the best ending. Circle it.

1. Sid became as green as the grapes he had stolen.

2. Sid did not become ill, but he never had a grape again, and he never stole again.

3. Sid planted a vine and gave his grapes to Mr. Green.

✎ Write about 3 kind things Sid could do to make up for stealing Mr. Green's grapes.

When two vowels come together, the **first** one is **long** and the **second** one is **silent**.

leaf

Sound out the letters to read each word.

| | | | |
|---|---|---|---|
| sea | meat | team | real |
| mean | read | meal | neat |
| seal | pea | year | beak |
| heap | lead | seat | weak |

| | | | |
|---|---|---|---|
| cream | speak | gleam | steal |
| heat | treat | tease | clean |
| leaf | grease | lean | sneak |
| season | creature | scream | please |

Learn to read these words:  **ocean  break  steak**

➜ Draw a line between the words that rhyme.

| beak | steal | | mean | lean |
|---|---|---|---|---|
| meal | week | | sneak | creek |

→ Match the words with their meanings.

___ 1. to heal        (a) to hit
___ 2. to fear        (b) to mend
___ 3. to beat        (c) to be afraid of

___ 1. grease       (a) fat
___ 2. East         (b) not fat
___ 3. lean         (c) opposite of West

___ 1. peak         (a) a sea animal
___ 2. meal         (b) top
___ 3. seal          (c) you eat it

___ 1. to scream    (a) not fake
___ 2. season       (b) to yell
___ 3. real         (c) a time of year, like spring

→ Circle the name of the picture.

| mean   meat | steal    real | speak    peak | seal    seam |
|---|---|---|---|
| meal    neat | lead    read | lead    beak | seat    sneak |
| heave   weave | tear    fear | sea    seal | East    heat |
| weak    heat | near    ear | flea    heal | eat    feat |

→ Choose a word from the list to complete each sentence. Write the word on the line. Then read the sentence to see that it makes sense.

1. Last year Mom went back _____ five times to be near her sick dad.

speaking

2. Their team is weak. We _____ them again today.

East

3. "Please listen, I am _____ to you!" said Ms. Bean.

squealed

4. The creature squeaked and _____ as Hilda picked it up.

beat

treat

5. "Let's have steak as a _____ today," said Martina.

eat

6. "It's best to eat _____ meat as it has less fat," said Mom.

lean

7. "Please _____ up your peas, dear," said Dad.

read

8. "Let's clean up the mess, and then I will _____ to you," said Dean.

→ Draw a line to the correct ending of each sentence.

1. Dave went swimming            as the sea.
2. The Beads spent the weekend   in the sea.
3. The ocean is the same         near the sea.


4. Will you leave                at five-fifteen.
5. The leaves                    me a snack?
6. The team will leave           fell from the tree.


7. I'll drink                    you a story.
8. I'll read                     to you again next week.
9. I'll speak                    a cup of weak tea.

# Anna at the Sea

 Read the story.

Learn to read this word: **her**

Anna was off to see the sea!
It was a long trip, but at last she got there.
"There's the sea! I can see the sea!" she screamed,
giving Mom and Dad a beaming smile. Then she:

➜ Put an X next to the sentence that tells what Anna did **not** do.

☐ Got **her** feet wet in the sea.

☐ Ran and leaped on the sand.

☐ Teased Dad by dropping a crab on his lap.

☐ Stepped on a snake and screamed.

☐ Hit **her** heel on a rock, making it bleed.

☐ Raked the leaves into a big heap.

☐ Dug a deep hole in the sand and went to sleep in it.

☐ Rubbed sunscreen on **her** skin.

✎ Write about 3 things you would do if you went to the sea.

# Creature

Read the story. See if you can find the 25 **ea** words. Circle them. Count each **ea** word even if it is repeated.

Learn to read this word: **eye**

It was the biggest, meanest creature Jean had ever seen. She was gripped by fear as the beast came near.

Its vast legs were the size of at least ten men and were as strong as steel. Its feet were immense. They trampled the trees as if they were sticks, and made deep prints in the mud.

The scales on its back gleamed as if they had been greased. Its tail beat from side to side. Its neck was like a snake and its black **eyes** stared at Jean.

Its ears flapped as the fantastic beast kept coming, its red beak seeking its next meal.

The creature kept on coming, coming, coming, until it came up close to Jean. She screamed.

Her screams woke up her dad.

"Help! Help! Leave me alone! Leave me alone!" she screamed as her dad came running in.

"It's OK, it's Dad. You must have been having a bad dream."

Jean sat up in bed. "Oh, yes," she agreed. It was a bad dream. I am glad to wake up!

→ Reread the story to answer the questions.

1. Find 2 words meaning **big** and write them on the lines.

_____     _____

2. The creature was (a) a seal (b) a weasel
   (c) a made-up animal

3. Draw a picture of the creature in the box.

✎ Write a story about an animal you make up.

→ Write the correct word on the line.

1. Let's _____ at six p.m.                    meat
   Jack doesn't eat _____.                    meet

2. Sandra _____ the drum.                     beats
   Neal had a big helping of _____.           beets

3. Glasses help me to _____.                  sea
   They swam in the _____.                    see

4. If you _____, you end up in jail.          steal
   _____ is a strong metal.                   steel

5. Bea undid the _____ of the dress.          seems
   "It _____ like it will rain today," Pete said.   seams

6. There are seven days in a _____.

The springs in the seat are _____.

weak

week

7. The _____ bit Hilda.

If you _____, you run away.

flea

flee

8. "You are a _____ to help me!" she said.

The _____ ate the grass.

deer

dear

9. "Will you cut up the _____s, please?"

"I have _____ there," he said.

been

bean

10. The grapes will be ripe at the _____ of the season.

Anna _____ed into the box.

peak

peek

11. The cut will not take long to _____.

He rocked back on his _____s.

heel

heal

12. Mildred got her _____ and bait, and
then went to the lake.

"A doll's not _____," she said.

reel
real

13. It's quite a _____ to eat six pizzas!
He put his socks on his _____.

feet
feat

14. Jan likes to _____.
Hong made a basket from the _____s.

reed
read

15. The bells _____ed at Danita and Juan's
wedding.

Jack's suntanned skin began to _____.

peal
peel

16. I hope you can find the _____.
Dad added _____s and carrots to
the meat in the pan.

leak
leek

## Lesson 21: Regular Double Vowel oa

When two vowels come together, the **first** one is **long** and the **second** one is silent.

coat

Sound out the letters to read each word.

| | | | |
|---|---|---|---|
| boat | road | loaf | soap |
| soak | foam | toad | oak |
| load | loan | coal | moan |
| goal | goat | toast | oats |

| | | | |
|---|---|---|---|
| float | groan | Joan | croak |
| cloak | cocoa | boast | roast |
| coast | throat | sailboat | coastline |

Learn to read these words:

**oar  roar  soar  board  broad  coarse  hoarse**

➔ Use one of the words listed above to answer each riddle. Write the word on the line.

1. It is a tree: _____

2. You can sail in it: _____

3. It means to lend: _____

4. If you get wet you become: _____ed.

5. It means to brag: _____

6. It makes a fire: _____

7. You can drink it: _____

8. It makes you clean: _____

→ Circle the name of the picture.

| | | | |
|---|---|---|---|
| coast | leaf | rod | milk |
| cost | loaf | road | mule |
| coat | oak | toad | moan |
| cake | oats | toast | meet |

| | | | |
|---|---|---|---|
| boat | fail | soak | vote |
| beast | feel | oar | note |
| boast | foam | soar | goat |
| bloat | float | roar | soak |

→ Write in the missing letter. Then read the sentence to see that it makes sense.

1. They got ___oaking wet in the rain.      j    p    s

2. "You do not need to ___oast. I got an A in the test, too," said Pedro.      g    b    f

3. "If you cut up the loaf and make the ___oast, I will make the cocoa," Dad said to Jean.      r    b    t

4. The ___ oat sailed up the coast.      c    b    g

5. "It's a ___oal! It's a ___oal!" yelled Ann, hoarse from screaming.      p    g    c

6. "The ___oast is clear, no one will see us," Jack said to Camilla.      t    r    c

7. Fine old oak trees lined the ___oad.      l    m    r

8. The __oads began to croak and Dan woke up.      s    t    l

# Joan's Day

Read the story.

See if you can tell if Joan is living at the present time, lived in the past, or is living in the future.

Learn to read these words: **with  your  you're (you are)**

Joan's mom woke her up at 6:00 a.m. Joan got up quickly and dressed. She put on her cloak and went to feed the pigs and hens. Next, she fed the mare a bag of oats. Then she milked the goats that were grazing in the grass. She plodded home **with** the pails of milk, but it began to rain and she got soaked.

Back home she flung off her cloak and cleaned herself up **with** hot soapsuds.

"I've fixed you a plate of ham and eggs and some oatmeal," her mom said.

"Thanks," said Joan. She had a cup of tea and cut the loaf of bread Mom had just baked. She ate her meal sitting by the log fire.

Then the clock struck 7:00. She got her slate. "Oh no, I'm late again!" she groaned, "Miss Croak will roast me alive. She gets mad if **you're** late."

She picked up her cloak, but it was still wet.

"Say, Mom, can I have **your** cloak?" she asked. "Mine's still soaking."

"Yes, dear," said Mom, smiling. It seemed she was always lending Joan her dresses and cloaks.

Joan put on her mom's cloak, kissed her, and ran off to meet her dad at the boat. As there was no road, Dad had to take Joan along the coast to the next bay to go to Miss Croak's classes.

Dad was loading six pigs onto the boat. He was taking the pigs to sell.

"Quick, Dad, I'm late!" said Joan.

Dad smiled and said, "You always say **you're** late, but you never are! **You're** OK, you've got loads of time."

He loaded the last pig on board the boat as Joan jumped in. Then he cast off, picked up the oars, and set off.

Joan's day always began like this, just as most kids' days began in 1840.

➜ Reread the story and circle the correct answer.

1. The story tells of (a) the present (b) the past
    (c) a time to come

2. Joan (a) had a meal and then did her jobs
    (b) did her jobs and then had a meal

3. Mom loaned Joan her cloak as (a) Joan's cloak got wet
    (b) Joan lost her cloak

4. Dad was selling six (a) goats (b) hens (c) pigs

5. It is safe to say (a) Joan arrived late at Miss Croak's
    (b) Joan arrived on time at Miss Croak's

➜ Reread the story. See if you can spot the 35 **oa** words. Circle them. Count each **oa** word even if it is repeated.

✎ Would you like to live in 1840 like Joan? Say why
or why not.

# An Ad

Read this ad and see if you can guess the product it is selling. The answer is an **oa** word. A product is a thing made by nature or humans.

Learn to read these words:  **that   this**

---

- Do you like products **that** keep you clean and make you feel great?
- Do you have to nag your kids to take a bath?
- Do you find it difficult to keep your house clean?

### *Then you need this product!*

It will keep you, your kids, and
your home

## clean, clean, clean.

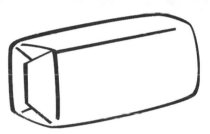

- It feels like soft satin and is slick as glass.
- It smells sweet.
- You don't need a lot.
- It fits into your hands.
- And it **does not cost a great deal!**

Just rub it on and stains will disappear—and so will your cleaning problems.

**It's fantastic! It's a must!**

## *Get it today!*

---

➡ Read the sentence and fill in the missing word.

The product is _____.

✎ Write your own ad for a product you like, such as a drink, a snack, or a game.

## Lesson 22: Regular Double Vowels ow and oe

When two vowels come together, the **first** one is **long** and the **second** one is **silent**.

bowl     toes

Sound out the letters to read each word.

**ow**   own     low     snow     grow
         bow     slow    crow     glow
         bowl    row     flow     mow
         owe     blow    tow      flown

blowing     grown     yellow       follow
widow       window    pillow       elbow
rainbow     hollow    snowflake    fellow

**oe**   toe    hoe    Joe    woe    foe

Learn to read these words:
know    borrow    sorrow    tomorrow

→ Match the words with their meanings.

___  1. to own      (a) to dig
___  2. to hoe      (b) to have


___  1. to stow     (a) to pack away
___  2. to mow      (b) to clip, cut


___  1. toes        (a) to pull
___  2. to tow      (b) they are on your feet

→ Add **ow** to find the name of each picture. Then write the number of the picture in the box.

☐ pill____    ☐ b____l    ☐ wind____    ☐ b____

☐ elb____    ☐ rainb____    ☐ cr____    ☐ m____

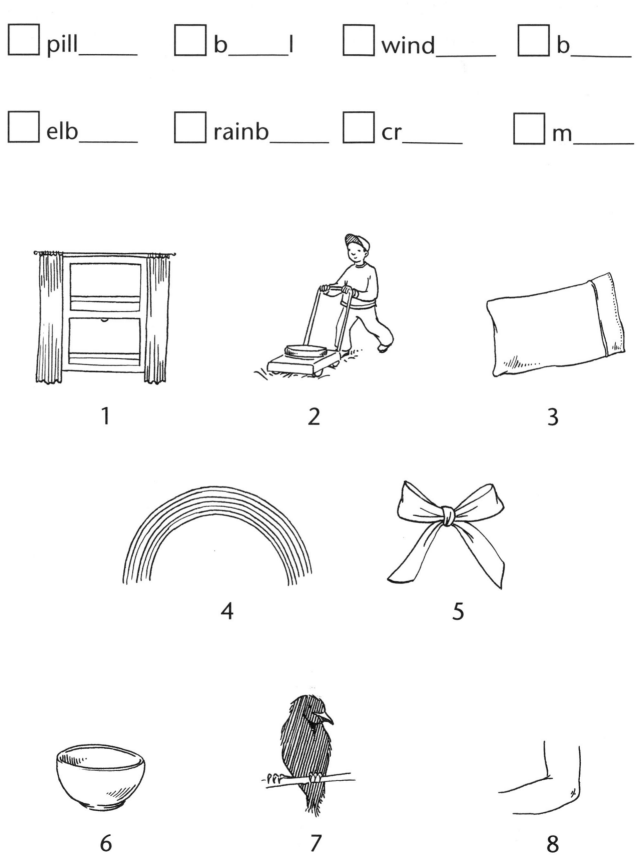

1

2

3

4

5

6

7

8

→ Find a word from the list to complete each sentence. Write the word on the line. Then read the sentence to see that it makes sense.

1. Mom closed the window. The wind was _____ the shades.

   follow

2. The sparrow's nest was hidden in the _____ of a willow tree.

   blow

3. "Well, you've grown into a big fellow!" exclaimed Granddad, _____ with pride!

   blowing

4. The cactus plant has _____ too big for the bowl.

   glowing

5. "If this wind keeps up, it will _____ the snow back on the steps," said Niles.

   grown

6. "Quick, _____ that fellow. He's stolen Ms. Fallow's bag," yelled Joe.

   hollow

→ Draw a line to the correct ending of each sentence.

Adam is as slow as a                          ox.
She eats like a                                snail.
That fellow is as strong as an                sparrow.

The kitten's coat is as soft and white as  bull.
She ran as straight as                           snow.
He bellowed like a mad                           a crow flies.

Her dress was as yellow as a                  arrow.
He was blowing his nose like a                lemon.
He went as straight as an                     trumpet.

# Snow

Look at the pictures. Then read the story. Under each picture write the number of the passage that tells about it.

_____

1.  "It's beginning to snow! I can see snowflakes on the windowpane," Joe exclaimed to June. "Let's make a snowman!"

"Yes, let's," said June.

"You may have to wait until tomorrow," Mom said. "You need a lot of snow to make a snowman."

2.  The next day the snow was deep. Joe and June went to the homes of their classmates and said, "Come and help us make a snowman. You'll need a spade. Do you have one?"

"No," said Edna," but we have a hoe, I'll bring that."

Santos said, "I can borrow a hoe from a fellow I know."

Luke said, "And I've got a sled we can use to tow the snow to the snowman."

Kim said, "I'll bring a big bowl and use that."

_____

3.    The kids met in the street and began to make the snowman. It was slow. It takes a lot of elbow grease to make a snowman!

At last Joe said, "He's great, let's dress him up."

_____

"I'll borrow Dad's bow tie," said Santos.

"I'll make him a row of buttons from stones," said Edna.

"I'll make 2 hollows and make him eyes from soda pop tops," said June.

"I'll make him a nose from a carrot and lips from twigs," said Kim.

"Dad owns a cap he never liked. I'll get it," said Joe.

4.    They dressed the snow-man. Then they had rides on Luke's sled. Kim fell off but she said, "It's great! The snow is as soft as a pillow!"

Next, they tried to hit the snowman's hat off. Joe missed and gave June a blow on the ear.

_____

5.    Then Santos missed and broke the window of the yellow home next to Joe and June's home. It belonged to Mrs. Bellow, a widow.

"Oh, dear! Let's run," exclaimed Jane.

But Santos said, "No, I'll have to tell Mrs. Bellow. And I'll have to pay her." Then he added, "But I can't. I'm broke! Can I borrow from any of you?"

"No, I'm broke, too!" said Joe and the rest.

Kim said, "I know. We can clear her snow. That will please her, and she may let you put off paying her back."

_____

6.    They did a great job clearing Mrs. Bellow's snow, and she was pleased. She gave them cake and hot cocoa, too.

She said the window was cracked and needed to be fixed.

_____

✎ Write your own story about a snowy day.

LESSON 22: REGULAR DOUBLE VOWELS OW AND OE

If a word or a syllable has **one** vowel and it comes at the **end**, it is usually **long**.

we        a-pron

Sound out the letters to read each word.

| a | ba-con | la-bel | ba-sin | ra-ven |
|---|--------|--------|--------|--------|
|   | Da-vid | va-cant | na-ture | ba-sic |

| i | si-lent | Fri-day | qui-et | i-tem |
|---|---------|---------|--------|-------|
|   | hi | pi-lot | fi-nal | li-on |

| o | go | o-pen | po-em | po-lite |
|---|----|-------|-------|--------|
|   | fro-zen | mo-ment | so | O-hi-o |

| u | mu-sic | fu-el | hu-man | cru-el |
|---|--------|-------|--------|--------|
|   | stu-dent | ru-in | u-nited | u-nit |

| e | me | be-gin | se-cret | fe-male |
|---|----|--------|---------|---------|
|   | e-ven | e-qual | re-play | de-frost |

| duet | pupil | retake | hotel |
|------|-------|--------|-------|
| poet | basic | bagel | radio |

Learn to read these words:  **do   don't (do not)
won't (will not)   is-land**

→ Draw a line between the beginning and the end of each word.

| a | pen | ba | cret | bro | ked |
|---|---|---|---|---|---|
| mu | pron | fro | el | na | ken |
| o | day | cru | zen | de | nal |
| Fri | sic | se | con | fi | frost |

| stu | gel | qui | gin | si | ment |
|---|---|---|---|---|---|
| e | qual | po | et | mo | ren |
| re | dent | tu | lite | ba | tend |
| ba | quire | be | lip | pre | sin |

| re | lot | re | man | ru | tel |
|---|---|---|---|---|---|
| na | nit | hu | on | re | in |
| u | play | po | fill | ho | et |
| pi | ture | li | em | di | peat |

→ Read the words. Circle the long vowel in each word. Then write the word, showing where it divides into syllables

evil ___e/vil___    silent _____

human _____    secret _____

David _____    item _____

poet _____    moment _____

defrost _____    pretend _____

cruel _____    label _____

→ Read the words. Then choose a word to complete each sentence. Write the word on the line.

**equal    vacant    final    items**

1. The kids played on the _____ lot.

2. Jock packed the _____ one by one into his suitcase.

3. Six plus six is _____ to five plus seven.

4. "This is the _____ time I will ask you to go to bed!" said Dad.

**moment    pretend    require    diet**

5. Her _____ has lots of grains and salad greens.

6. "Can you wait a _____?" asked Hector. "I won't be long."

7. Let's _____ we're in a play and dress up," said Jen.

8. Do you _____ any help?" the man asked.

# Evil Island

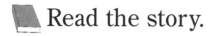 Read the story.

Aliens have stolen the casket containing the secret of human life. They have hidden it on Evil Island, an island so evil no living being can remain alive on it long.

Elaine has been sent to find the casket and bring it back. If she does not find it, human beings will die.

Elaine landed on Evil Island at Devil's Cove. She crossed the Vacant Grasslands and came to Cruel Pond. She peered into the pond, but the casket was not there. She went on and came to the ruins of a big home. She hunted in the ruins, but she did not see the casket.

She plodded on and then she came to Violet Grotto. She gazed into it to see if the casket was at the bottom, but it was not. She strode on until she came to a vast lake. It was full of crocodile bones but there was no casket.

Time was passing. Elaine did not have long. She ran past an immense volcano. Smoke and flames **erupted** from its open top. She felt its great heat and said to herself, "It is too hot. Even the Aliens can't get near the volcano." She then spied the Coconut Grove. She tramped between the trees but still did not find the casket.

Time was passing. Elaine was afraid the evil of the island was creeping up on her. At last, she arrived at the **base** of Steep Hill. She made her way up, passing dens that lions had lived in long ago. At last she got to the top and there in a deep cave was the casket!

She picked it up and ran straight back to her boat at Devil's Cove. Elaine's life was safe, and so were the lives of human beings.

→ Reread the story and find these words:  **base**  **erupted**

Then match the words with their meanings.

_____ 1. base      (a) bottom

_____ 2. to erupt   (b) to rise up

→ Read the map and the details explaining the way Elaine went. Then make a line showing the way she went and put an X on the spot where she located the casket.

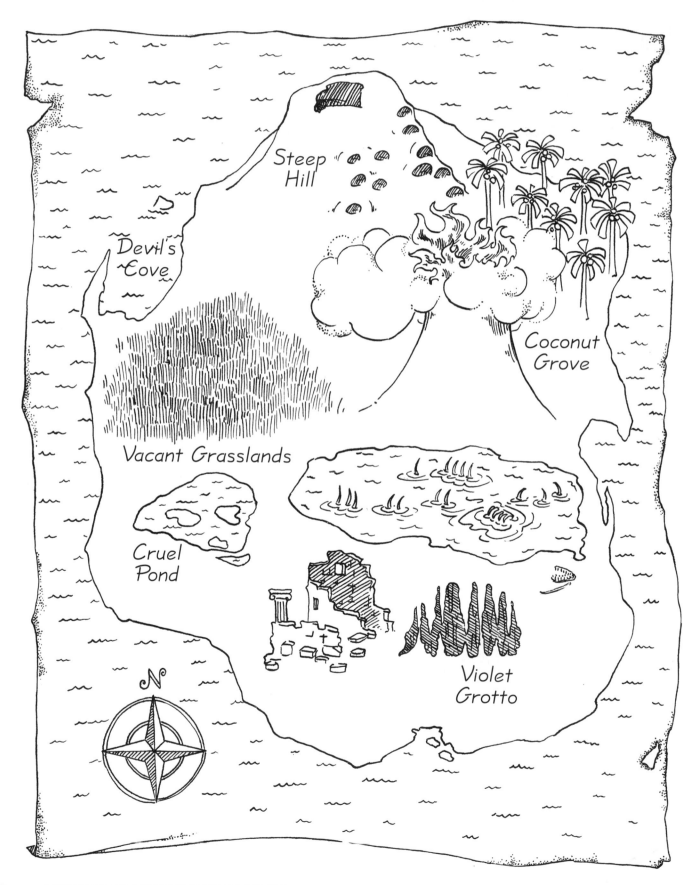

Steep Hill

Devil's Cove

Coconut Grove

Vacant Grasslands

Cruel Pond

Violet Grotto

N

✎ The story was about an evil island. Write a story about an island that is full of fun and happiness. Tell what it is like and what you can do there.

# Eating Well

One of the secrets to human life that the Aliens stole must have been to **eat well**.

Look at the 4 pictures. They show the 4 kinds of products you need to eat well.

Read the sentence and fill in the missing word. The first syllable ends with a vowel.

The best _____ is made of equal helpings from the 4 products in the pictures.

Read the menus of David, Jason, and Lisa's meals. Did they eat well?

**Jason**

*7:30 a.m.*
a bagel
pancakes
lemonade

*12:00 p.m.*
hot dog and bun
cake
soda pop

*6:30 p.m.*
fried ham
baked potato
frozen peas
pecan pie

**David**

*7:30 a.m.*
hot oatmeal
a muffin with jam
milk

*12:00 p.m.*
pizza
cream pie
soda pop

*6:30 p.m.*
meat loaf
yams
potato salad
milk pudding

**Lisa**

*7:30 a.m.*
bacon and eggs
toast
melon
milk

*12:00 p.m.*
carrot sticks
chopped beef and a bun
grapes

*6:30 p.m.*
baked salmon
potatoes
green beans
tossed salad
plum pie
milk

➜ Now read the questions and circle the correct answer.

1. Did Jason eat well?     yes  no

2. Did David eat well?     yes  no

3. Did Lisa eat well?     yes  no

| | |
|---|---|
| To read a long word you need to break it into **syllables**. A word has as many syllables as it has **vowel sounds**. | 2  a-pron<br>3  mon-u-ment<br>4  dan-de-li-on |

➡ Say the name of the picture. Then write in the box the number of syllables you hear.

Remember: There is only **one vowel sound** when:
1. There is a **silent e**.
2. Two vowels come together and the **first** one is **long** and the **second** is **silent**.

cake   time

rain   tree
soap   grow

→ Circle the vowels and write the number of vowels in each word. Then write the number of vowel sounds and syllables in the word.

| | Vowels | Vowel sounds & syllables | | Vowels | Vowel sounds & syllables |
|---|---|---|---|---|---|
| b(a)sk(e)t | 2 | 2 | wait | ____ | ____ |
| even | ____ | ____ | potato | ____ | ____ |
| way | ____ | ____ | soak | ____ | ____ |
| blowing | ____ | ____ | awoke | ____ | ____ |
| deepen | ____ | ____ | bacon | ____ | ____ |
| life | ____ | ____ | sleep | ____ | ____ |
| season | ____ | ____ | locate | ____ | ____ |
| consonant | ____ | ____ | great | ____ | ____ |
| cube | ____ | ____ | coastline | ____ | ____ |
| detail | ____ | ____ | Wisconsin | ____ | ____ |
| graduate | ____ | ____ | secret | ____ | ____ |
| closed | ____ | ____ | cure | ____ | ____ |
| load | ____ | ____ | window | ____ | ____ |
| seat | ____ | ____ | mile | ____ | ____ |

When the same **two consonants come together** in a word, divide the word between the two consonants.

can-not
mit-ten

→ Circle the vowels. Then divide each word into syllables with a slash mark. Then write the number of syllables in the word.

| Syllables | | Syllables | | Syllables | |
|---|---|---|---|---|---|
| r(a)b/b(i)t | 2 | wettest | ___ | rotten | ___ |
| borrow | ___ | hidden | ___ | follow | ___ |
| puppet | ___ | muffin | ___ | sudden | ___ |
| biggest | ___ | lesson | ___ | tomorrow | ___ |
| pillow | ___ | cassette | ___ | beginning | ___ |
| happen | ___ | bottom | ___ | mitten | ___ |

→ What kind of vowel comes **before** the same two consonants? Circle the correct answer.

(a) long          (b) short

→ Choose a word from the list to complete each sentence. Write the word on the line.

1. "You may _____ my bike if you like," said Bettina.

rotten

2. "This is the _____ tomato I have grown," Mike said with pride.

borrow

3. "Is it a hand or a string _____?" Luis asked.

cassette

4. "I can't eat this melon, it's _____," said Coretta.

hidden

5. Lee played the _____ Mom had just given him.

biggest

6. "I hope it doesn't rain as we have a game _____," said Oscar.

puppet

7. "I can't find the left shoe. I suppose Spot has _____ it again," said Emmett.

tomorrow

Remember: If a syllable has **one** vowel and it comes at the **end**, the vowel is usually **long**.

go    re-peat

If a syllable has **one** vowel followed by **only consonants**, the vowel is **short**.

hand    hap-pen

➜ Circle the vowels in each word. Divide the word into syllables with a slash mark. Then write **l** for long, **s** for short, and **x** for silent over the vowels.

les/son          cupcake          raindrop          frozen

homemade    gallon          inside          campfire

traffic          coat          strongest          himself

music          student          common          begin

crayon          basement          bowl          robot

attic          Sunday          explain          increase

→ Draw a line between the beginning and the end of each word.

| You can put these on. | | | These help you tell the time. | |
| --- | --- | --- | --- | --- |
| stock | ket | | o' | ment |
| mit | coat | | mo | ond |
| jac | ing | | sec | ute |
| rain | ten | | min | clock |

| These are living beings. | | | You can eat these. | |
| --- | --- | --- | --- | --- |
| ani | sect | | mel | cake |
| in | man | | cup | con |
| rep | mal | | ba | meal |
| hu | tile | | oat | on |

| You can play these. | | | These are animals. | |
| --- | --- | --- | --- | --- |
| trum | olin | | li | el |
| vi | jo | | cam | bit |
| ban | pipes | | rab | ten |
| bag | pet | | kit | on |

Read the story.

Learn to read these words:  **instead**  **someone**

Today many animals, and even humans, are afraid of bats. But many years ago, this was not so. In fact, the animals teased bats and made fun of them.

In those days bats were like rats as they did not have wings. But their legs were not as long and strong as the legs of rats. They could not run fast. In fact, they were the slowest of animals.

They were weak and **frail**, too. They did not see well. Their ears were too big. And they had the **unusual habit** of hanging by their toes.

This story tells how bats got their wings.

One day, as the animals were picking on Bat as usual, Nature came along.

"I must have a meeting," she said. "I need help."

The animals met by a big oak tree and Nature said, "I need **someone** to take a note to a land that is a long way away. You will need to be brave and fearless. And, I must tell you, you may not come back alive."

The animals were quiet. Not one of them said a thing, not even the fast deer, the cunning fox, the strong lion, or the long-legged camel. "The note must be taken today," Nature said, "so please, will one of you do it?"

Still the animals remained silent.

"Please," Nature pleaded, "the note must go today."

Again, not one of the animals spoke up. They were too afraid to go on the fearful trip.

At last, Bat raised her hand and, trembling with fear, squeaked, "I-I'll g-go."

The rest of the animals grinned and smiled. But Nature did not.

"Bless you, Bat," she said, "I am so grateful."

Then she said, "Come to me."

Still trembling, Bat went to Nature, expecting Nature to give her the note.

**Instead**, she held Bat's hand in hers and said, "You are going to help me, so I am going to help you."

Then she pulled Bat's fingers and, to her amazement, they began to grow. Next, Nature cut two wide strips from her fine silk dress and lay them across Bat's hands.

Then she fastened the strips to Bat's fingers.

Next, she picked up Bat and tossed her way up to the top of the oak tree!

Was Bat amazed again!

Bat's hands waved and flapped in panic. She expected at any moment to land at the base of the oak tree and be killed. But instead, she began to soar up, up, up. It was fantastic!

At last, Bat glided back to the oak tree. She landed beside Nature and said, "Give me the note and I will take it."

But **instead** of giving Bat the note, Nature smiled and said, "There is no note." Then she repeated to the rest of the animals, "There is no note. I was just testing you to see if you were **selfless** and kind. You did not pass the test, but Bat did. To repay her, I have given her a present that bats will always have."

And from that day on, bats have always had wings.

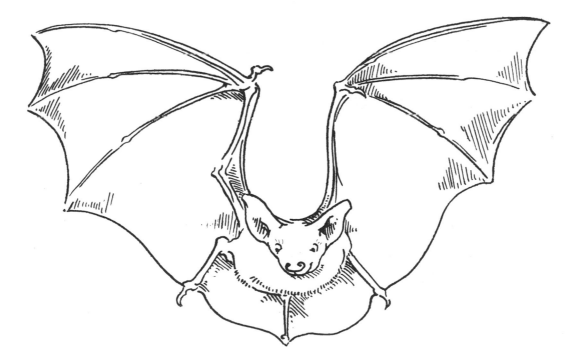

→ Circle the correct answer.

1. Bat was selfless. What does that mean?
   (a) soaring to the top of a tree
   (b) flapping and waving your hands
   (c) helping someone instead of yourself

2. The story tells of
   (a) the animals teasing Bat
   (b) Nature being unkind to the animals
   (c) Bat getting wings

3. Nature said she needed an animal to take
   (a) a box
   (b) a packet
   (c) a note

4. To go on the trip, Nature said the animal had to be
   (a) big and strong
   (b) slim and fast
   (c) brave and fearless

5. Nature made Bat's wings from
   (a) leaves from the oak tree
   (b) her dress
   (c) a silk web

→ Put the sentences in the order that they come in the story.

_____ The animals met by a big oak tree.

_____ In those days bats were like rats.

_____ You did not pass the test, but Bat did.

_____ Next, she picked Bat up and tossed her way up
to the top of the oak tree!


→ Reread the story and find these words: **unusual  habit**

Now match the words with their meanings.

_____ 1. habit        (a) odd, not usual
_____ 2. unusual      (b) doing often


→ Choose one of the words to complete each sentence. Write
the word on the line. Then read the sentence to see that it
makes sense.

1. Mr. Jones is in the _____ of getting up
at 6:00 a.m.

2. It is _____ to have a pig as a pet.

✎ Write your own story about a bat.